LEARN TO
READ AND WRITE

Alphabet Workbook

Volume 2 • 2016

heritagetexts@gmail.com

ISBN: 978-09894213-4-8

Draw pictures of words that begin with letter ***t***

Write the letter ***t***.

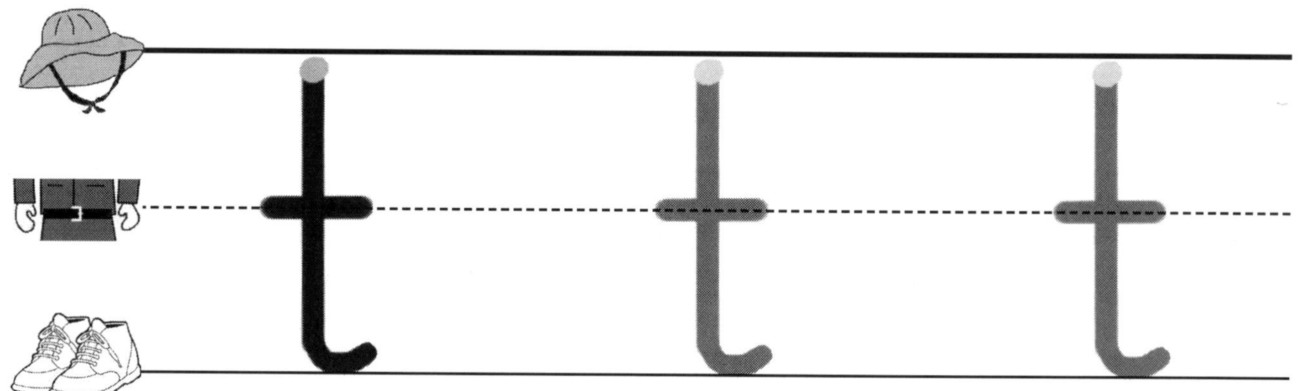

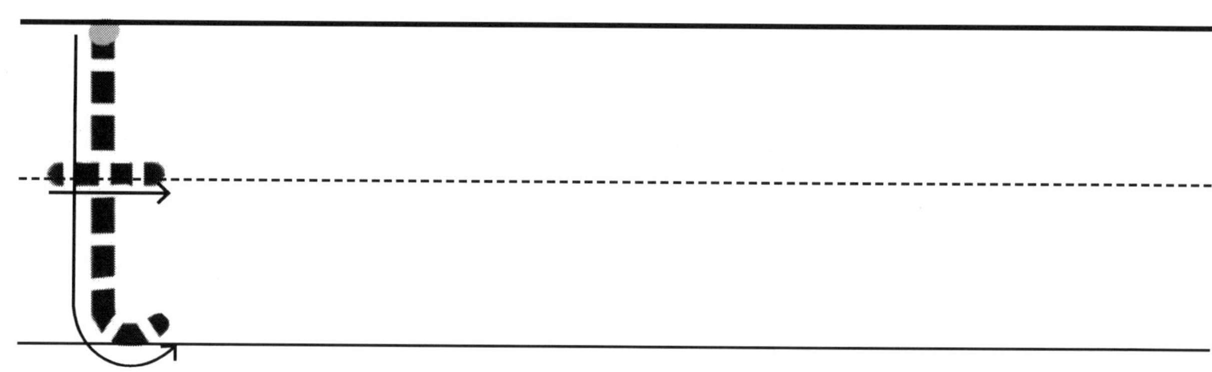

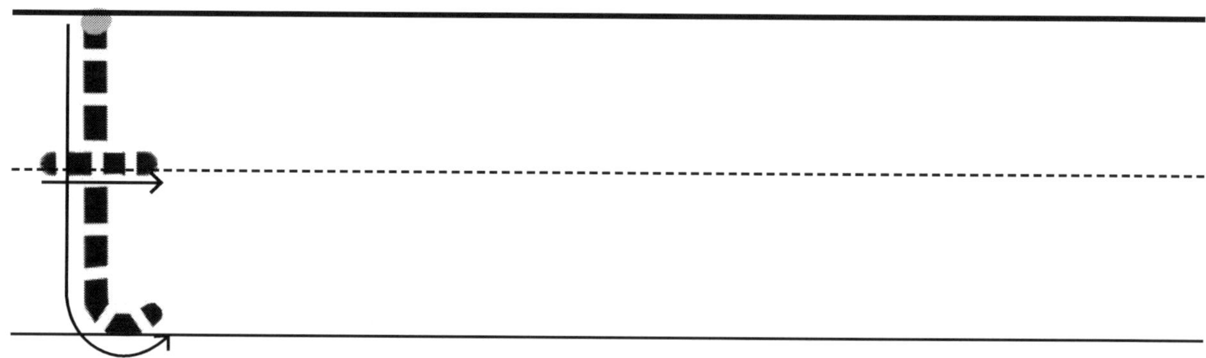

Write the letters ***t***, ***s***, ***p***, and ***d***.

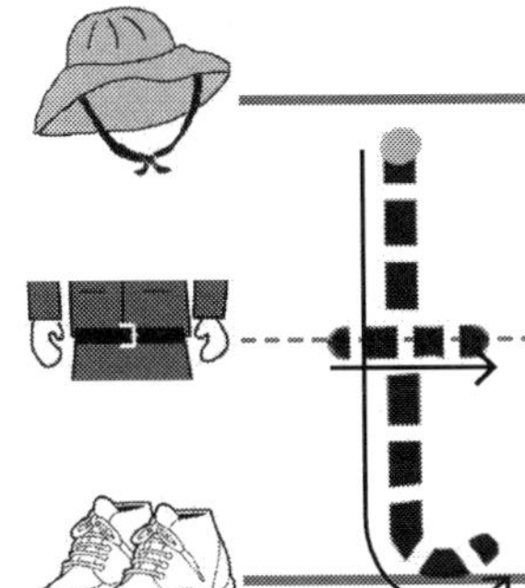

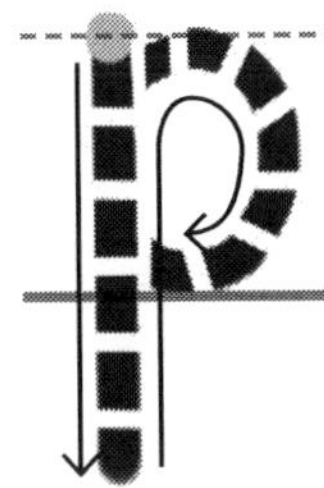

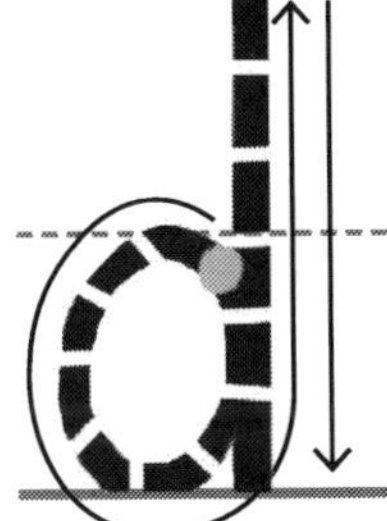

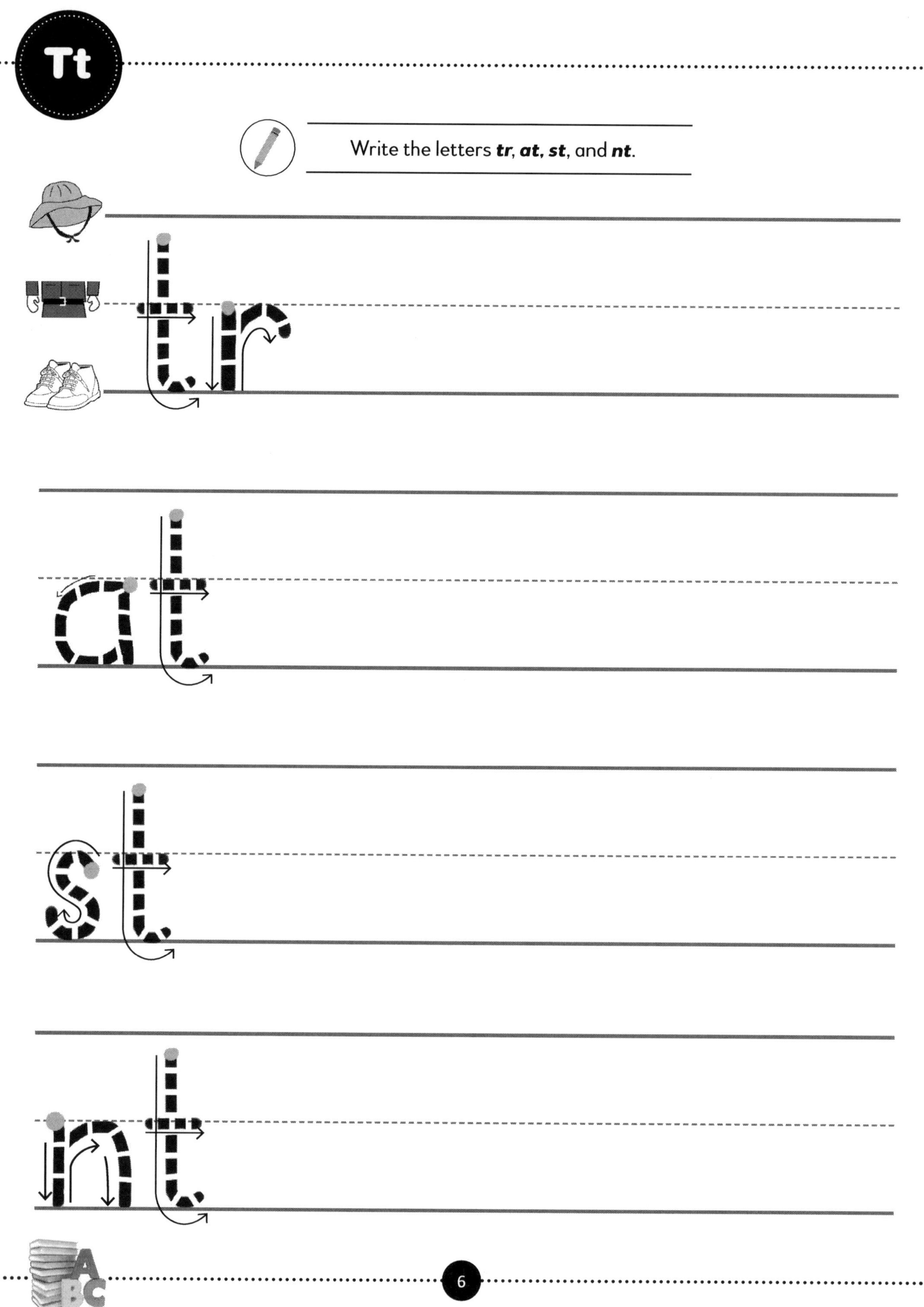
Tt
Write the letters ***tr***, ***at***, ***st***, and ***nt***.
tr
at
st
nt

Write the letters ***Tt***. Say the word that names each picture.
Color the picture whos name begins with the same sound as ***turtle***.

Tt

Name ______________________________

Tt

Say the name of each picture. Color the picture whose name has the same ending sound as ***hat***. Write the letter ***t***.

Name ______________________

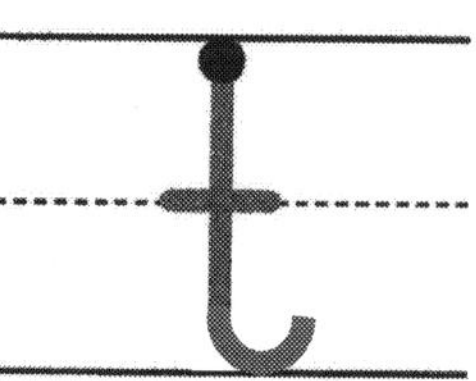

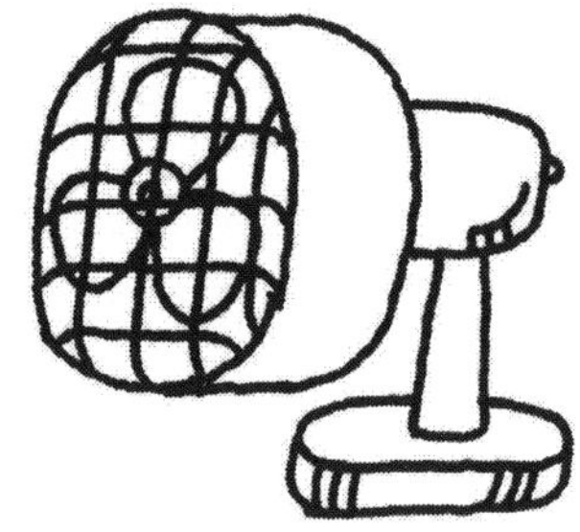

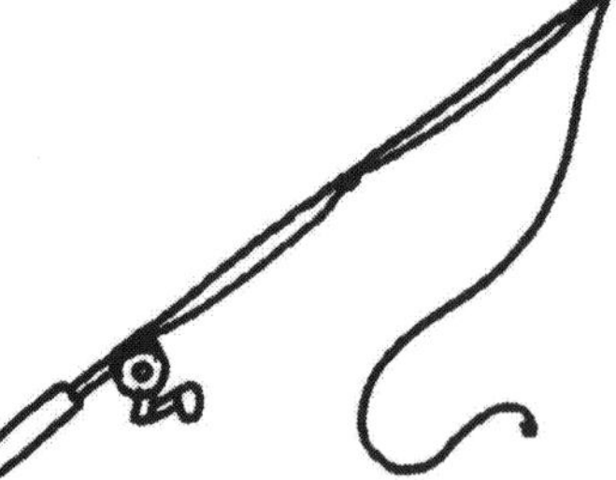

Say the name of each picture. Where do you hear the sound /t/**t**? Draw a circle around the first **t** if it is the beginning sound (as in turtle). Draw a circle around the second **t** if it is the ending sound (as in hat).

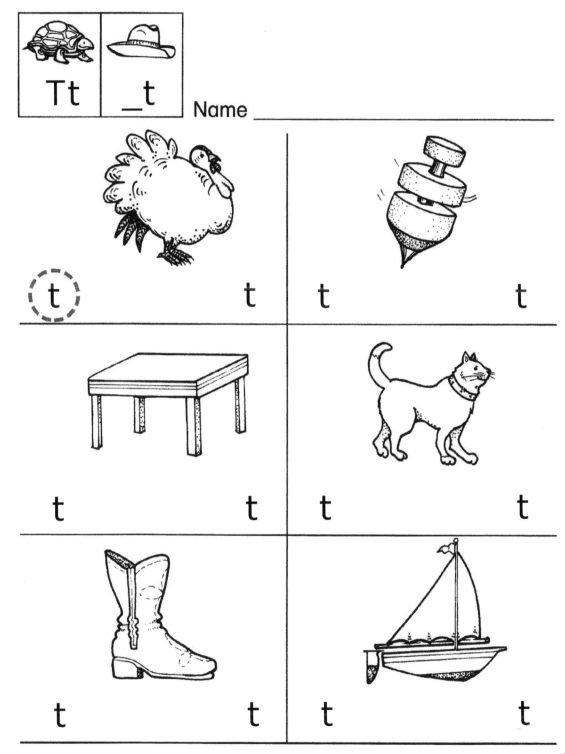

Tt	_t

Name ____________________

t	t	t	t
t	t	t	t
t	t	t	t

Name each picture. If the picture begins with the /t/ sound, draw a line to the tiger. If it ends with the /t/ sound, draw a line to the goat.

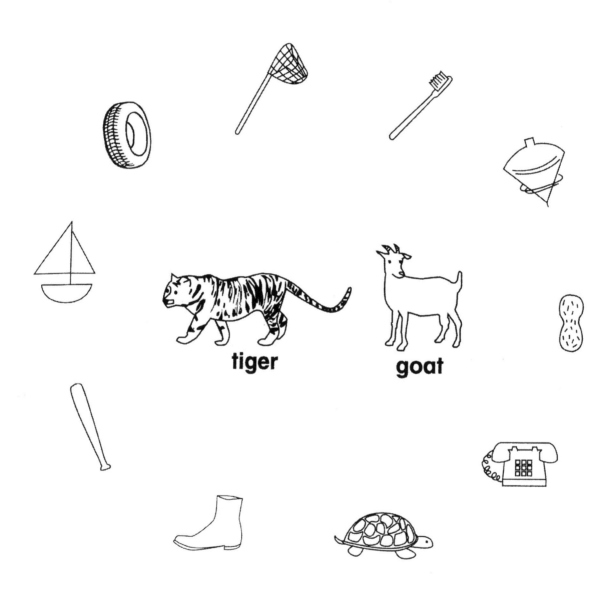

tiger

goat

Cut out the pictures and sort them on the following page.

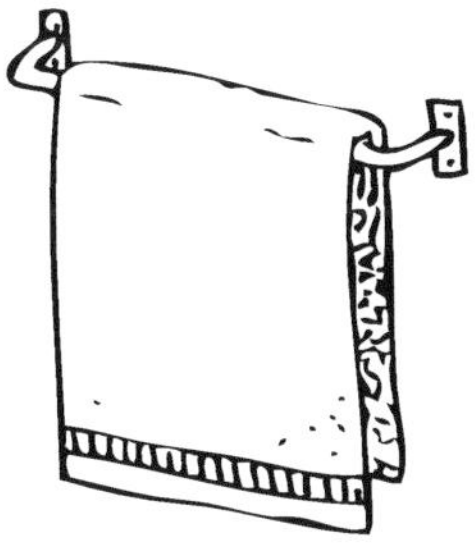

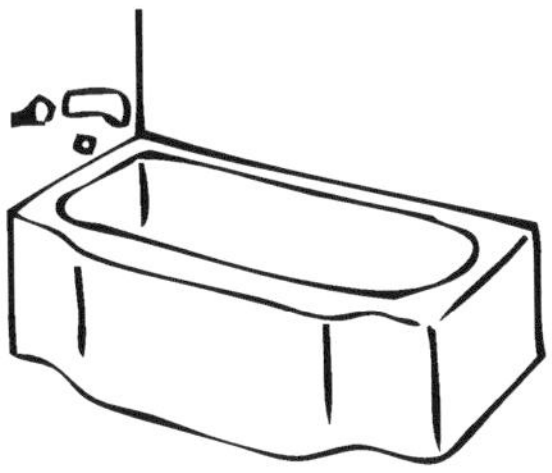

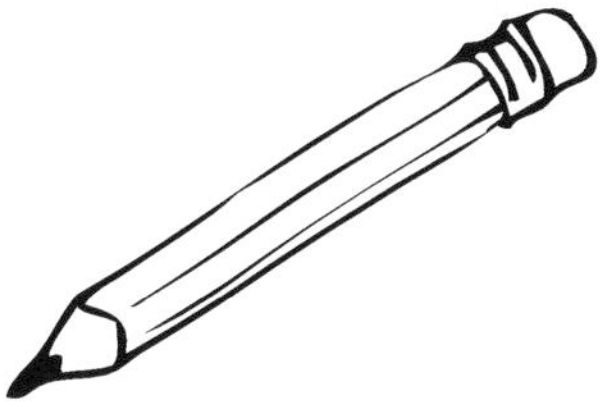

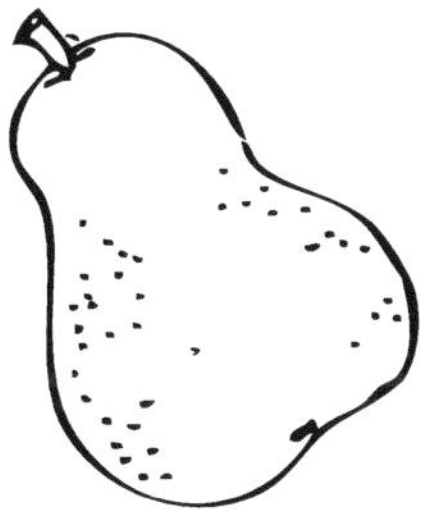

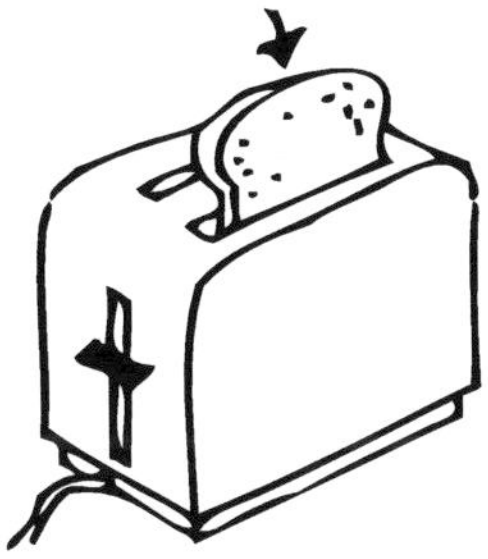

Pp	Tt

Read the words and draw a picture.

p a t

r a t

m a t

t a n

Cut out the pictures and sort them on the following page.

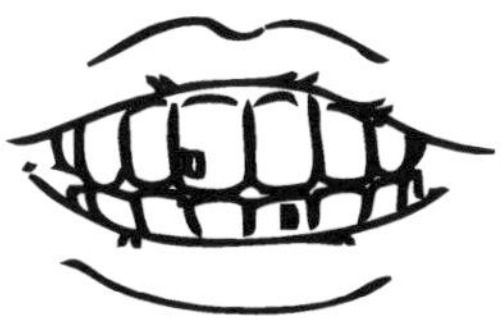

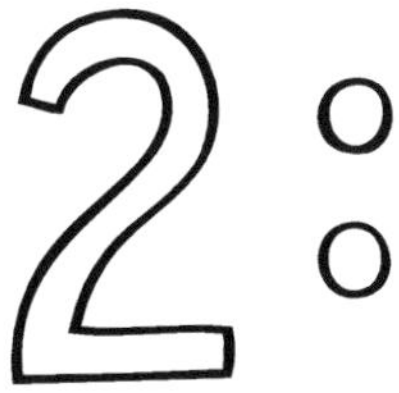

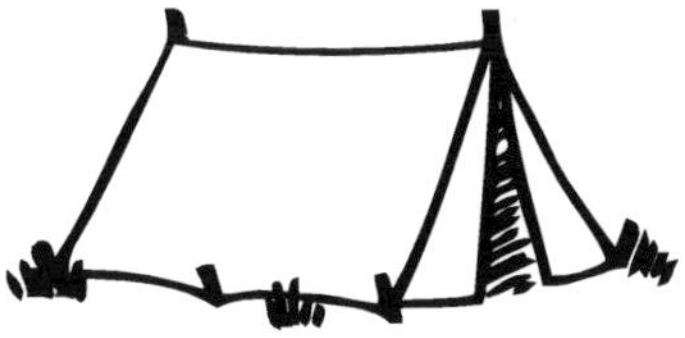

Dd	Tt

Read the word, tap out the ***sounds*** of the word. Then, circle the ***number*** of sounds and write the word on the line.

tan	1 2 3 4 5	
tad	1 2 3 4 5	
Nat	1 2 3 4 5	
sat	1 2 3 4 5	

n	t
t	r
d	s
m	d
p	p
s	m

Cut on the dotted line in the word frame below.

Cut out the strips of letters on the dotted lines only. Make words by passing them through the slits on the word frame.

[ ] a [ ]

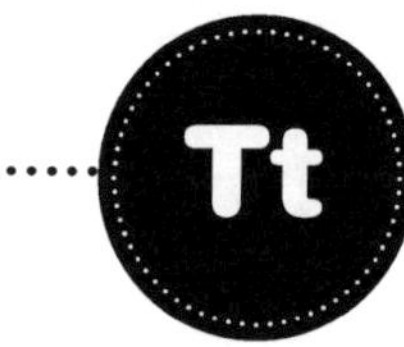

Cut out the ***letters*** on the top. Paste them into the spaces on the bottom that are missing letters to make ***words***.

n	r	d	r	d	m
p	s	t	n	p	t

	a		
	a		
	a		
	a		
	a		
	a		

like

we

Read the sentences using the words and pictures.

I like  .

I like  .

I like  .

Read the sentences using the words and pictures.

We like .

We like .

We like .

Read the sentences by saying the words and telling about the pictures. Draw a line under the word ***we*** in each sentence.

Name ____________________________________

We 

and we   .

We 

and we .

Read the word at the ***beginning*** of each row. Draw a circle around same word that you find in the row.

Name ____________________

is	in	is
said	said	and
I	A	I
is	and	is

Read the words. Draw a circle around the word ***and***. Draw a circle around the word ***I***.
Draw a circle around the word ***is***. Draw a circle around the word ***said***.

Name ______________________________

I　　and　　is

and　　said　　I

is　　and　　said

I　　said　　and

Say the ***first*** word in the row. Draw a circle around the word where you see it in the same row.

Name ______________________________

I	I	the
and	said	and
said	said	the
is	is	I

Read the word at the ***beginning*** of each row. Draw a circle around same word that you find in the row.

Name ____________________

the	we	the
said	said	and
we	I	we
the	said	the

Read the words and sentences.

1. sad
2. Sam
3. sap
4. pass
5. mass
6. mat
7. tan
8. tap
9. pat
10. sat

1. Sam.
2. Sam sat.
3. Sam sat <u>on</u> <u>a</u> mat.
4. <u>Is</u> Sam sad?

1. Tam
2. Tam <u>said</u> pass the pan.
3. <u>We</u> pass the pan.

Tt

Read the sentences below with ***sight*** words underlined.

1. My dad is mad.

2. I like my tan pad.

3. Ann said we ran.

4. Pam likes the rat.

5. Ann is not at my mat.

6. I tap and rap.

7. I like it a tad.

8. The sap is on that map.

Look at the pictures. Write a **1** in the box that shows what happened ***first***.
Write a **2** in the box that shows what happened ***second***.
Write a **3** in the box that shows what happened ***third***. Then, color the pictures.

Look at the pictures. Write a **1** in the box that shows what happened ***first***.
Write a **2** in the box that shows what happened ***second***.
Write a **3** in the box that shows what happened ***third***. Then, color the pictures.

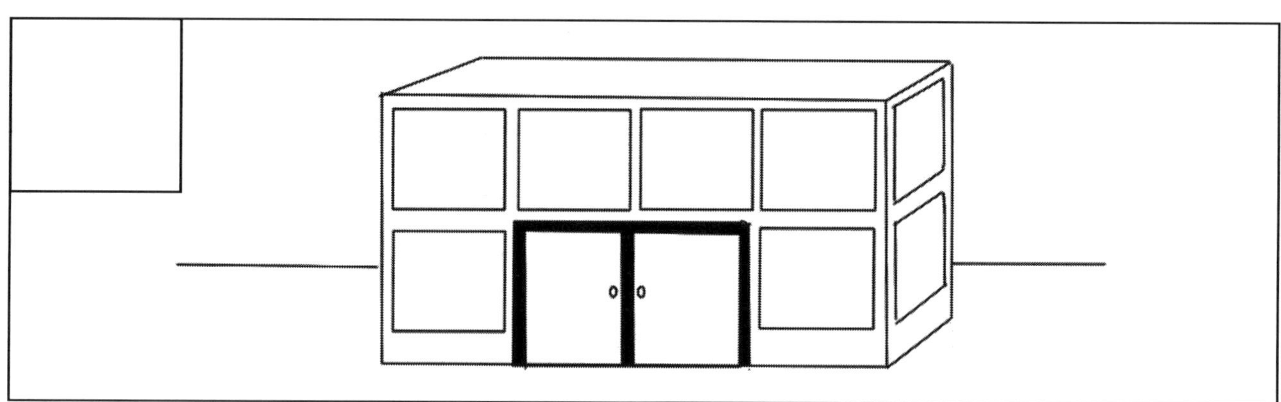

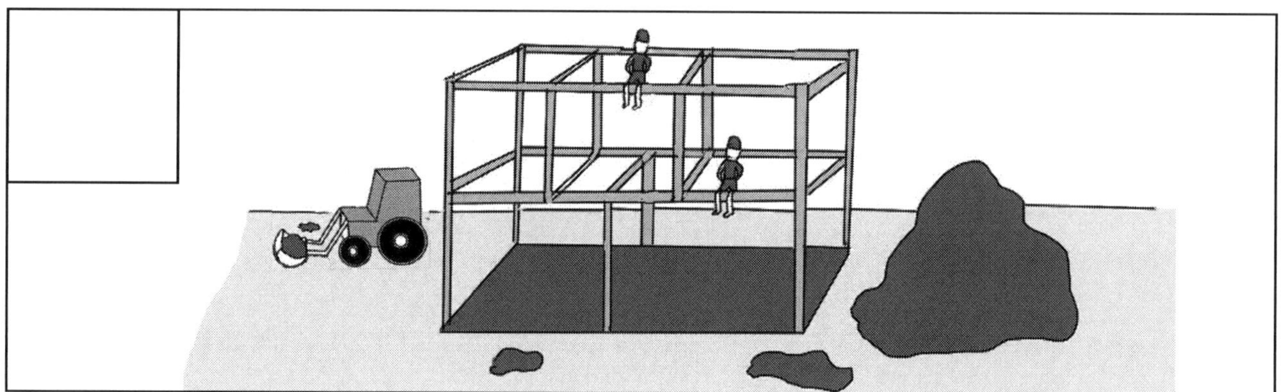

Look at the pictures in each row. Think about the ***story*** they tell. Draw a circle around the small picture at the end of each row that shows what will happen ***next***. Then, color the picture.

Look at the pictures in each row. Think about the story they tell. Draw a **circle** around the small picture at the end of each row that shows what will happen next. Then, **color** the picture.

Look at the pictures. Think about the story they tell.
Write a **1** in the box that shows what happened **first**.
Write a **2** in the box that shows what happened **second**.
Write a **3** in the box that shows what happened **third**.

☐ Sam raked the leaves.

☐ Jan jumped into the pile of leaves.

☐ There was a big pile of leaves.

☐ The balloon popped!

☐ Joe blew up the balloon.

☐ Joe had a small balloon.

Look at the pictures. Think about the story they tell.
Write a **1** in the box that shows what happened **first**.
Write a **2** in the box that shows what happened **second**.
Write a **3** in the box that shows what happened **third**.

☐ The butterfly flew away.

☐ The cocoon began to open.

☐ You could see the butterfly.

☐ Watch out for the peel!

☐ May I have a banana?

☐ That banana was good!

Draw pictures of words that begin with letter ***g***

Write the letter ***g***.

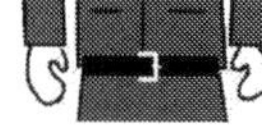

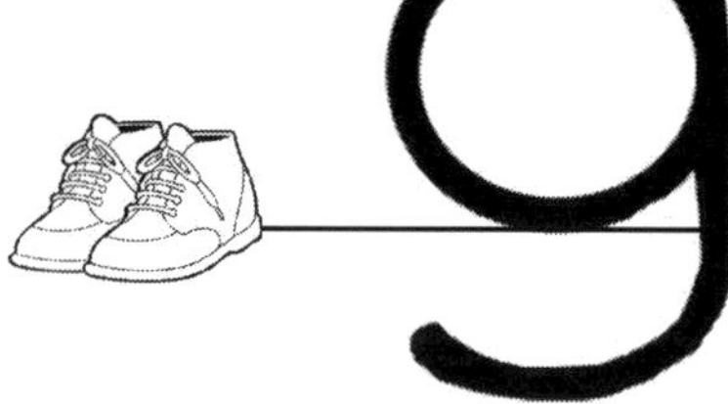

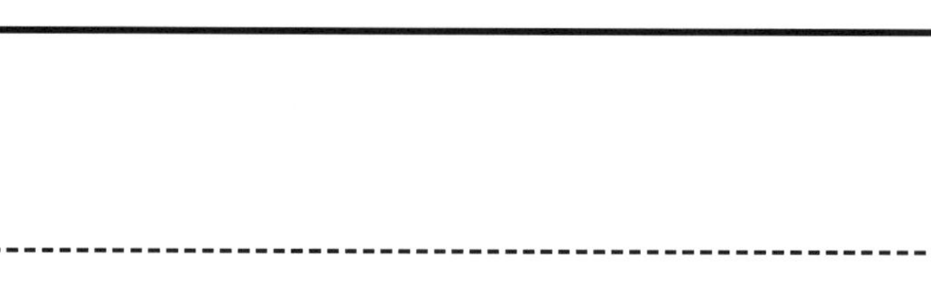

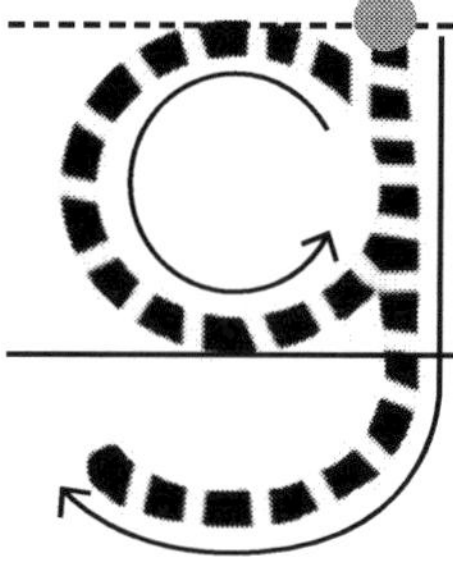

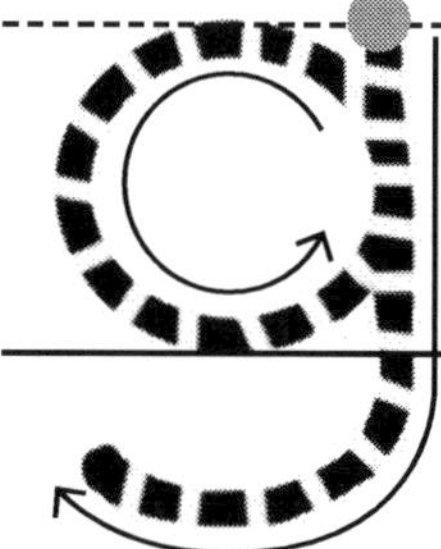

Write the letters ***g***, ***t***, ***m***, and ***s***.

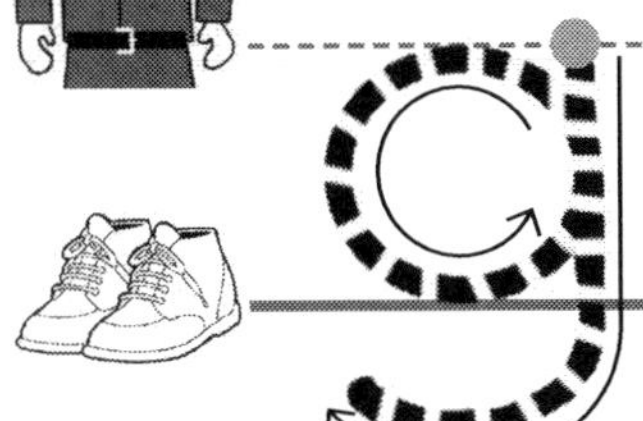

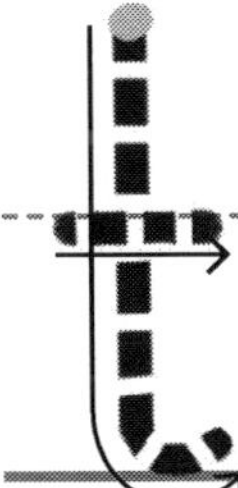

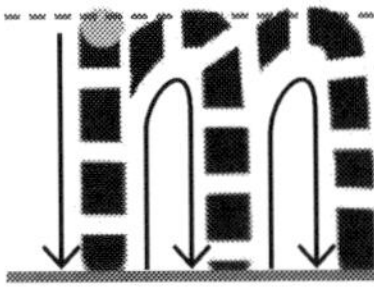

Write the letters ***tag***, ***gr***, ***ng***, and ***rag***.

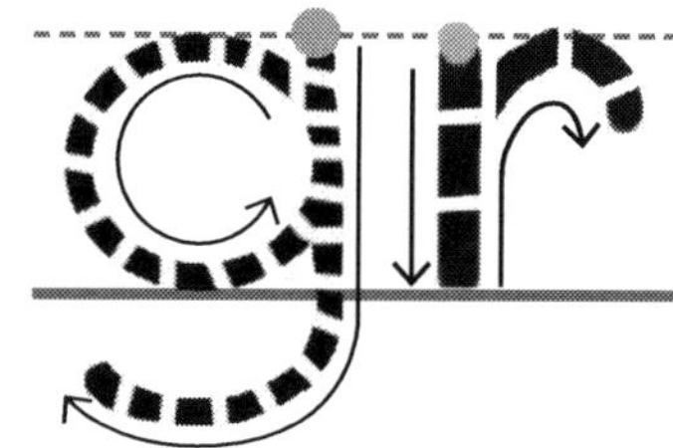

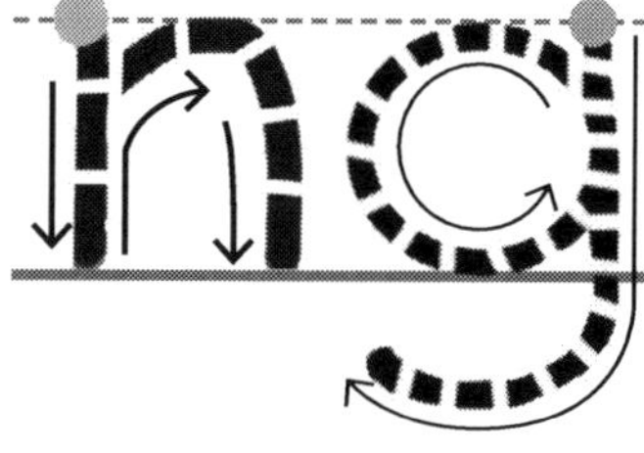

Trace the letters ***Gg***. Say the word that names each picture.
Color each picture whose name begins with the same sound as ***gift***.
Draw a line from these pictures to the letters ***Gg***.

Name ______________________________

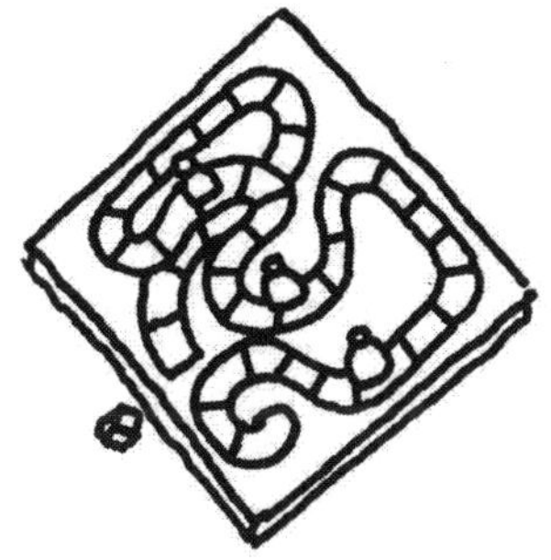

Say the name of each picture. Write the letter ***g*** under each picture that has the same ending sound as ***frog***.

–g

Name ______________________

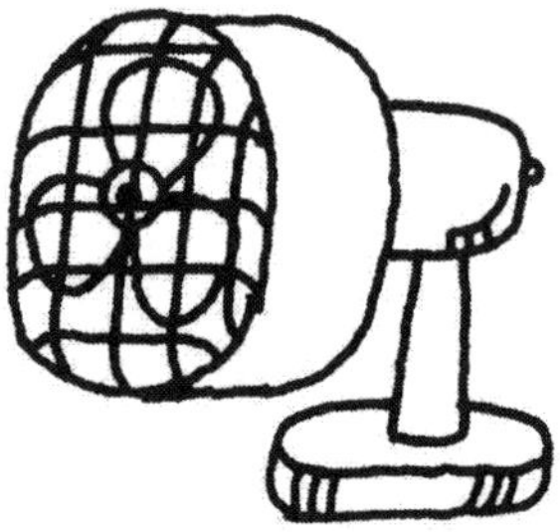

g

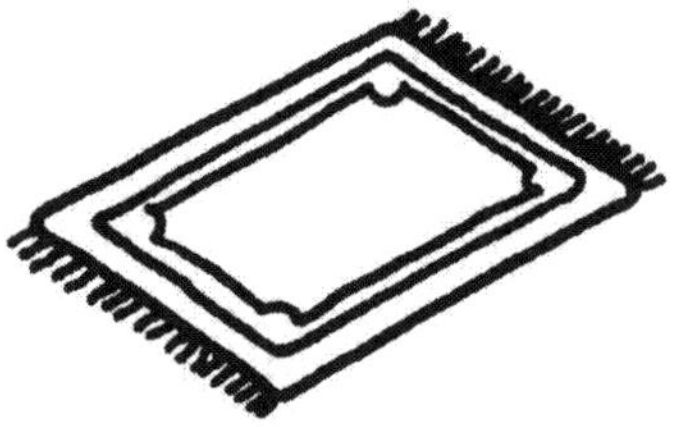

Say the name of the picture. Where do you hear the sound /g/***g***? Draw a circle around the first ***g*** if it is the beginning sound (as in ***gift***). Draw a circle around the second ***g*** if it is the ending sound (as in ***frog***).

Gg | –g

Name ____________________

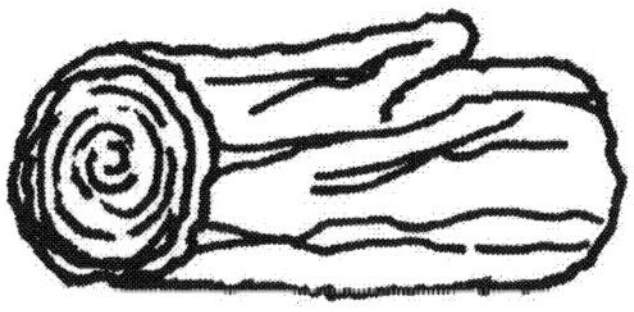

1. g g

2. g g

3. g g

4. g g

5. g g

6. g g

Name each picture. If the picture begins with the sound /g/, draw a line to the girl. If it ends with the sound /g/, draw a line to the bag.

girl **bag**

Name each picture. If the picture begins with the sound /g/, draw a circle aroung the first ***g***. If it ends with the sound /g/, draw a circle aroung the second ***g***.

1.	2.	3.
g g	g g	g g

4.	5.	6.
g g	g g	g g

7.	8.	9.
g g	g g	g g

Read the word, tap out the ***sounds*** of the word. Then, circle the ***number*** of sounds and write the word on the line.

gas	1 2 3 4 5	
gap	1 2 3 4 5	
sag	1 2 3 4 5	
nag	1 2 3 4 5	

Cut out the vowel. Paste it onto a stick. Use the stick to practice blending the vowel before and after each consonant.

a

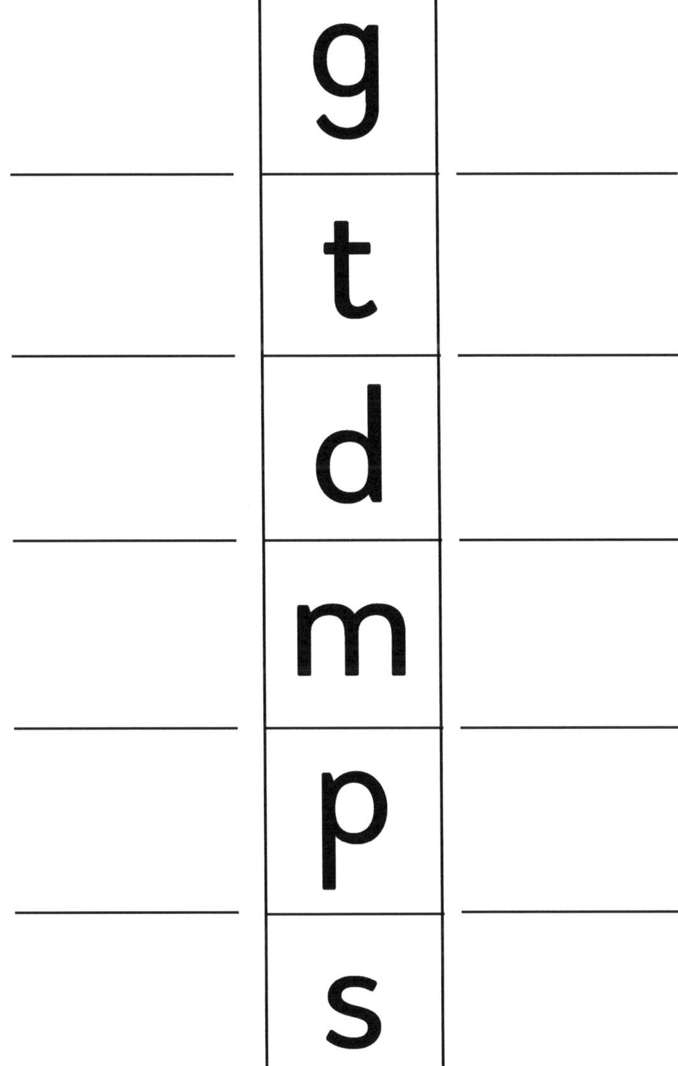

Cut out the letters on the left. Paste them into the spaces on the right that are missing letters to make words.

Make Words

s	n	a
r	m	a
g	g	a
g	t	a
p	g	a

Color the letter that is ***different***.

P

R

p

Draw a circle around the letter pair that is ***different***.

CJ GI CJ CJ

KO KO KO GT

XS XS PR XS

LP TE TE TE

Circle the picture that is ***different***.

Circle the picture that is ***different*** in each group.

Circle the picture that is ***different***.

Circle the picture that is ***different*** in each group.

Circle the picture that is ***different***.

Circle the picture that is ***different*** in each group.

Circle the picture that is ***different*** in size.

Circle the letter pair that is ***different*** in each row.

BB DD DD DD

CC CC OQ CC

LM LM LM LN

SP SS SS SS

Circle the letter pair that is ***different*** in each row.

YE YE VY YE

IJ JJ IJ IJ

FF FF FF FE

GH GA GH GH

Circle the letter pair that is ***different*** in each row.

II IH II II

MN MN MN NN

UJ VJ UJ UJ

AZ AZ AN AZ

Color the capital ***G***s green. Color the lower case ***g***s grey.

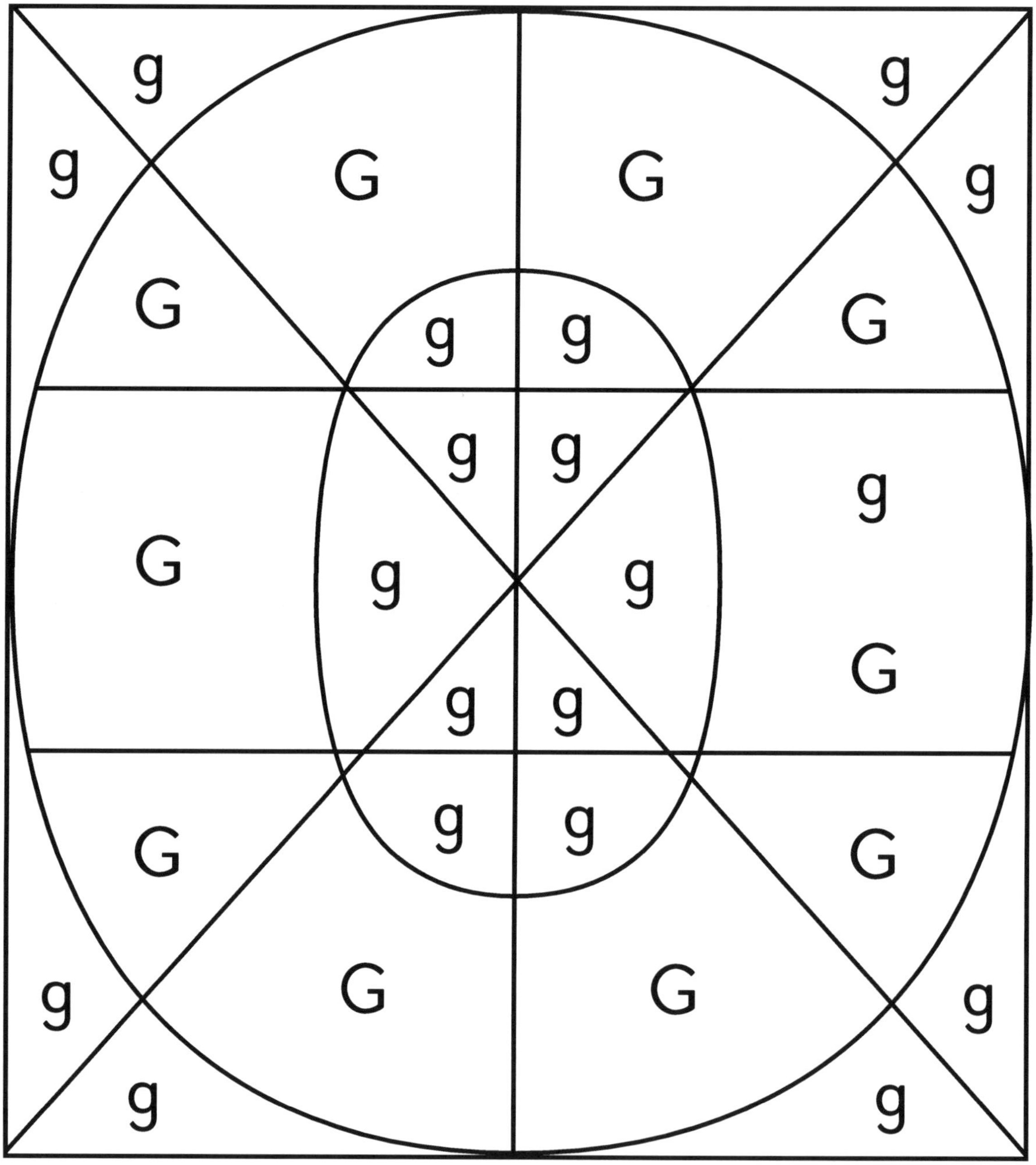

g g

g G G g

G g g G

g g g

G g g

G

g g G

G g g G

g G G g

g g

 Draw pictures of words that begin with letter ***c***

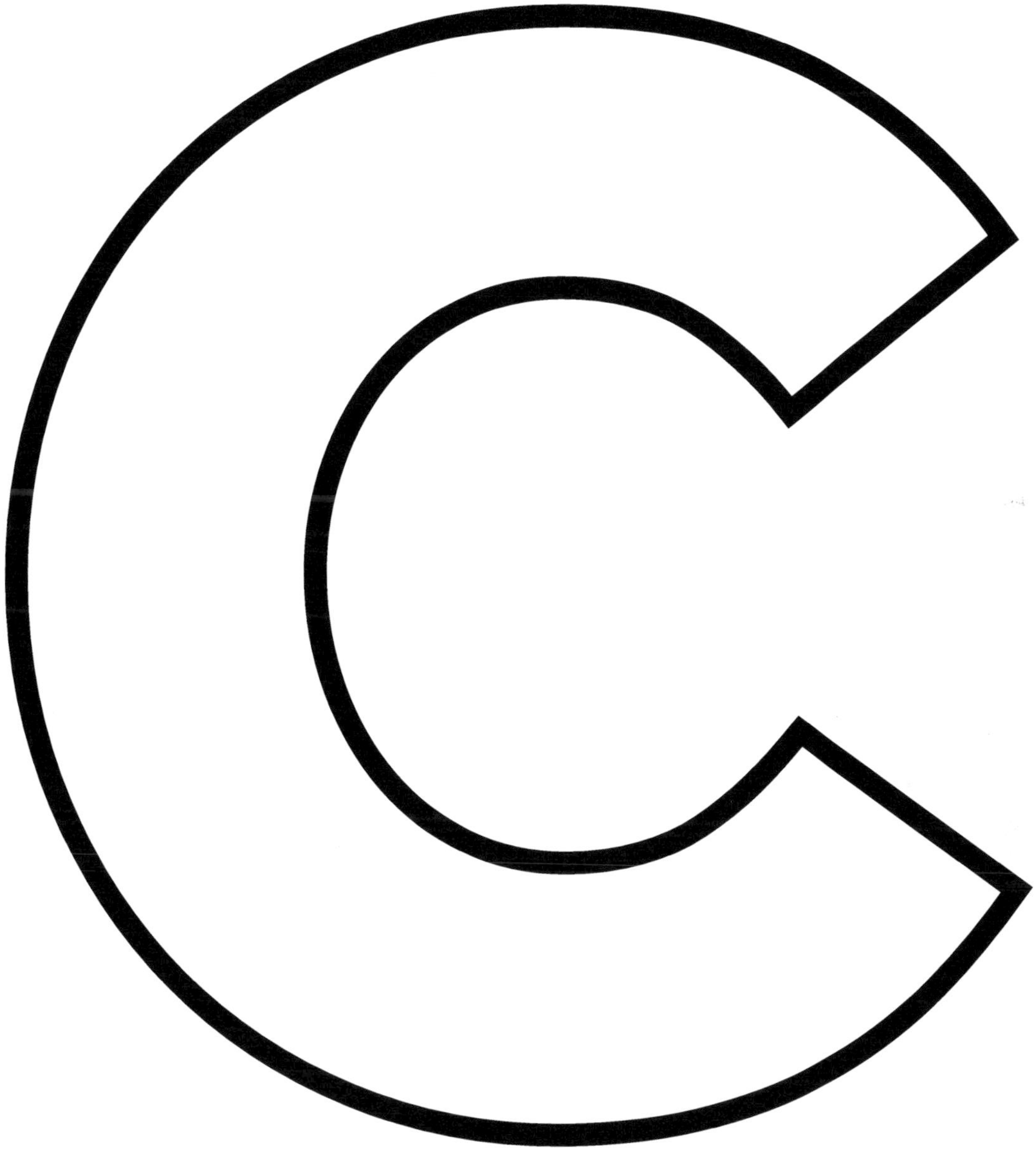

Cc

Write the letter *c*.

c c c

c

c

Write the letter ***c***, ***g***, ***t***, and ***s***.

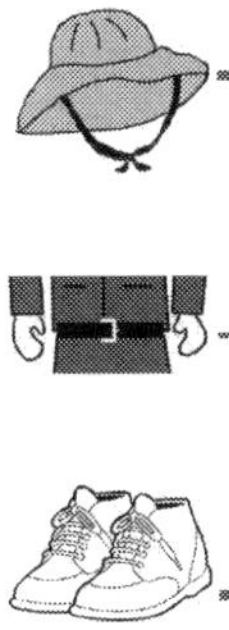

c

g

t

s

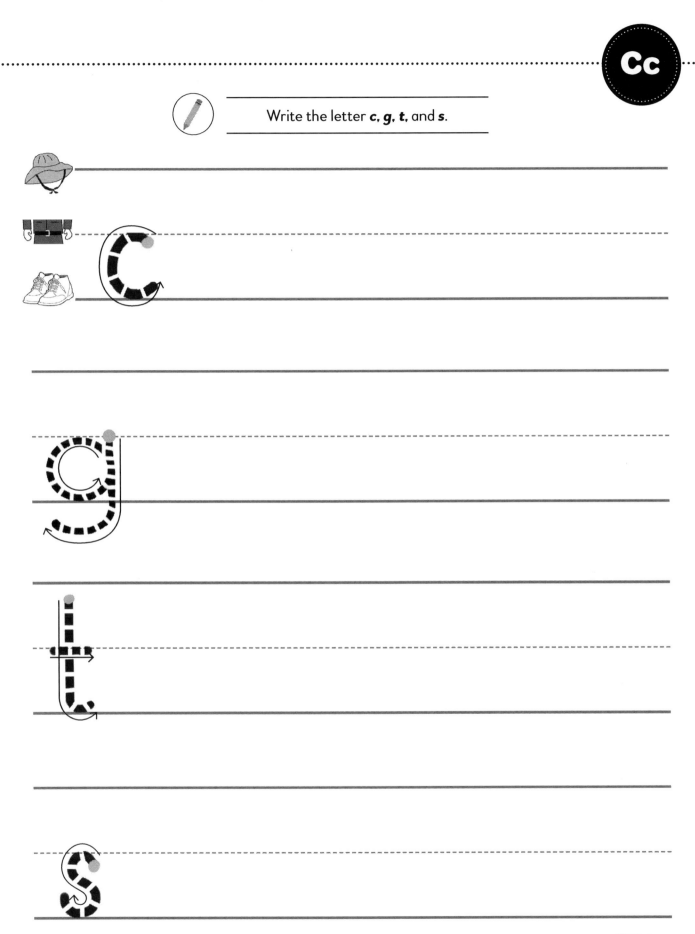

Write the letter ***cr, cap, cat,*** and ***can***.

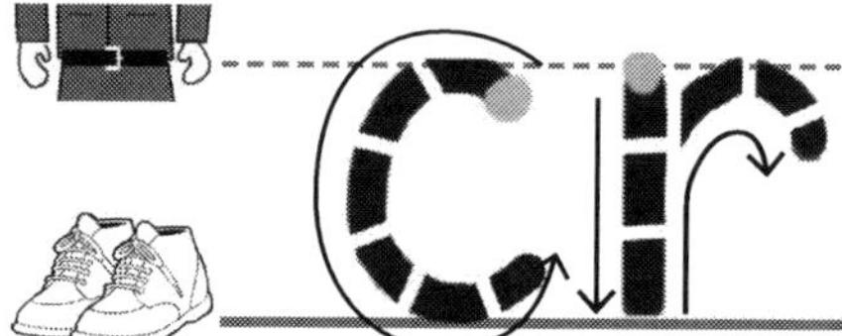

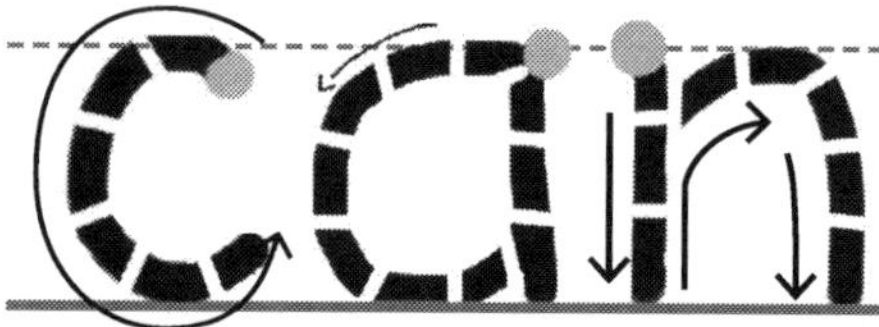

Write the letter ***cast*** and ***grass***.

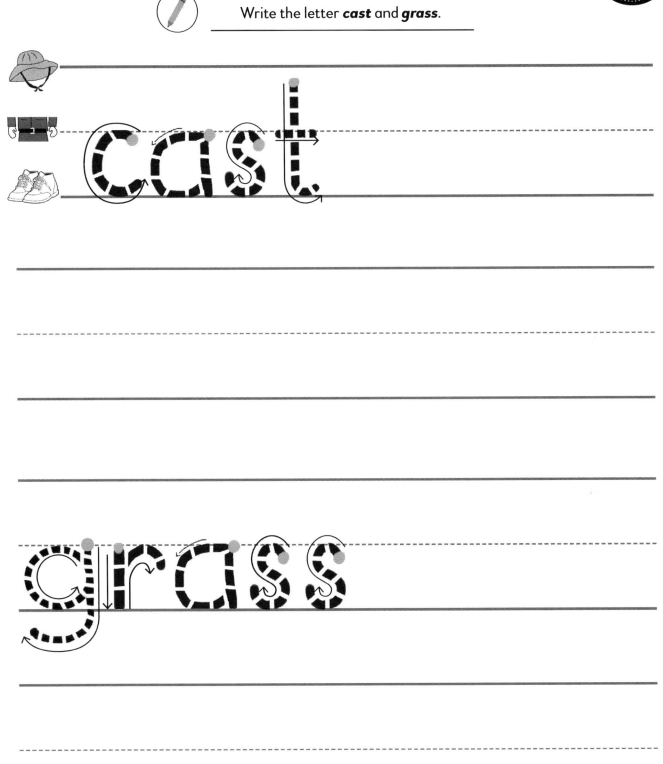

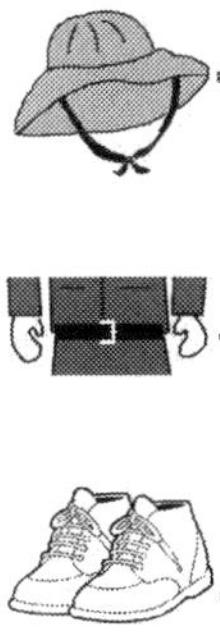

cast

grass

Trace the letters ***Cc***. Say the word that names each picture. Color each picture whose name begins with the same sound as cap, and draw a line from these pictures to the letters ***Cc***.

Name ______________________________

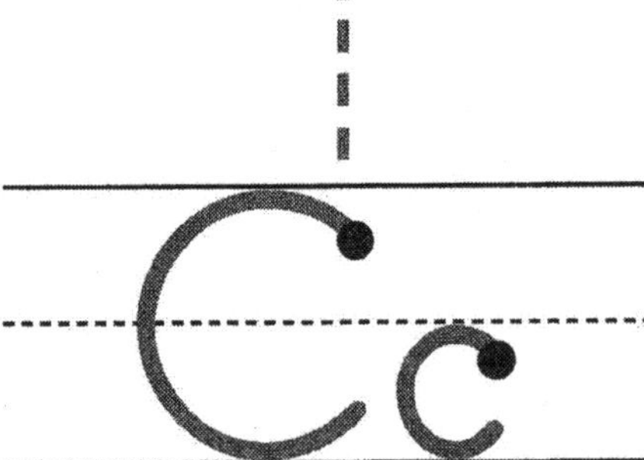

Name the pictures in each row. Color the pictures whose names begin with the sound for ***c***.

1.    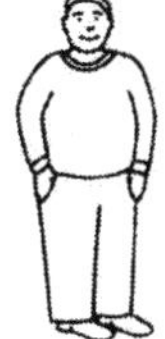

2.    

3. 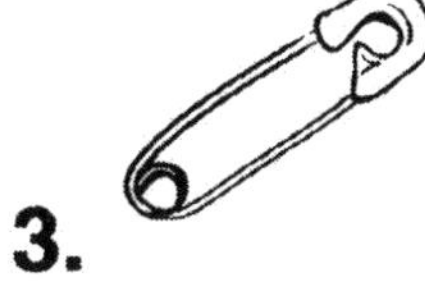   

4.  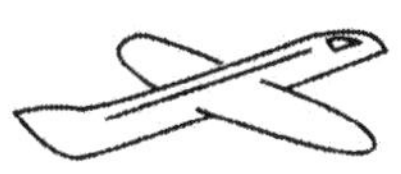 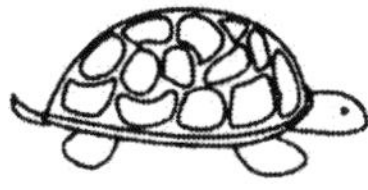 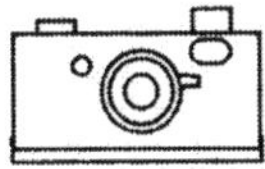

5.    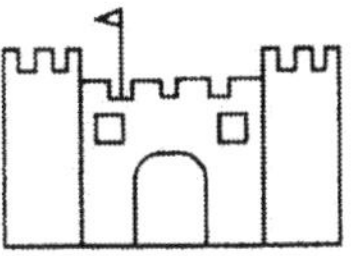

Cut out the vowel. Paste it onto a stick. Use the stick to practice blending the vowel before and after each consonant.

a

____	g	____
____	t	____
____	d	____
____	m	____
____	p	____
____	s	____
____	c	____

Cut out the letters on the left. Paste them into the spaces on the right that are missing letters to make words.

Make Words

s	n	t
r	p	t
s	d	t
p	s	n
r	m	d
s	d	n

	a	g
	a	g
g	a	
	a	d
c	a	
c	a	
c	a	

Cut out the pictures and sort them on the following page.

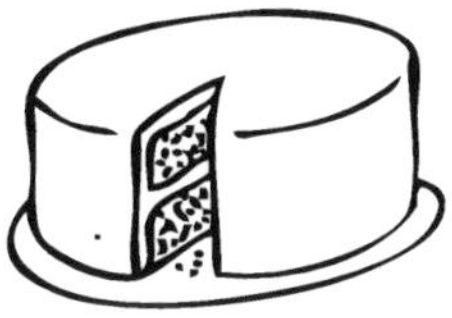

Cc Gg

Cut out the pictures and sort them on the following page.

Ss Cc

Ss	Cc

Read the words in each house.
Fill in the name of the family in the roof.

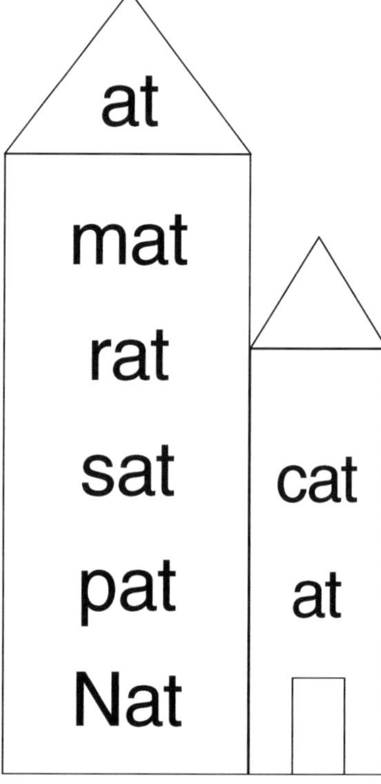

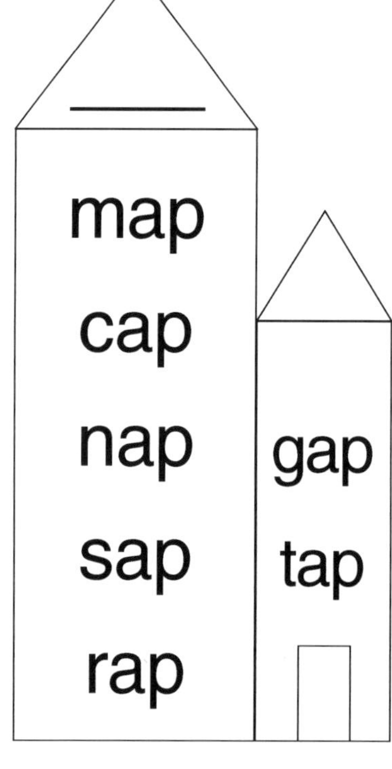

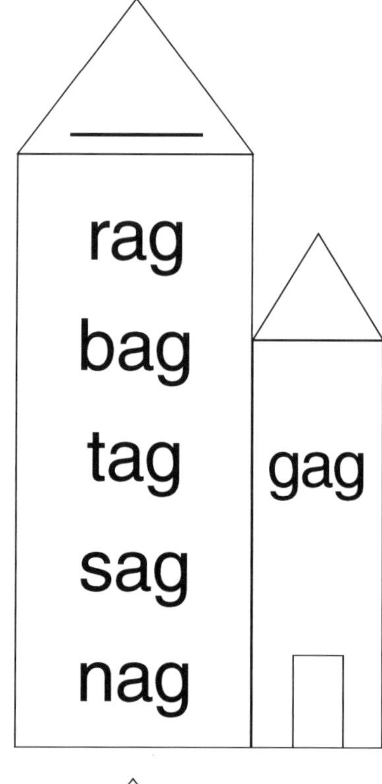

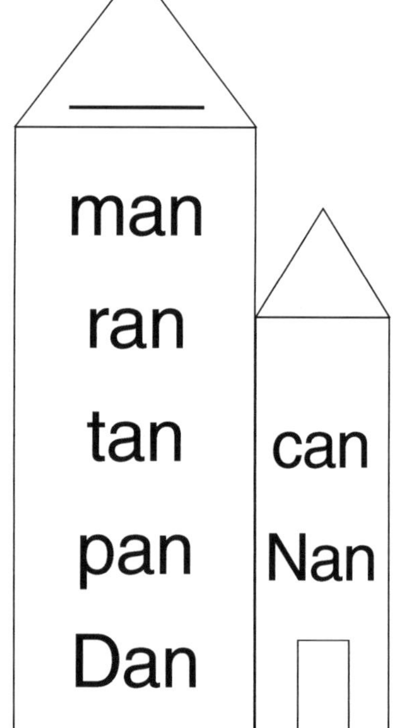

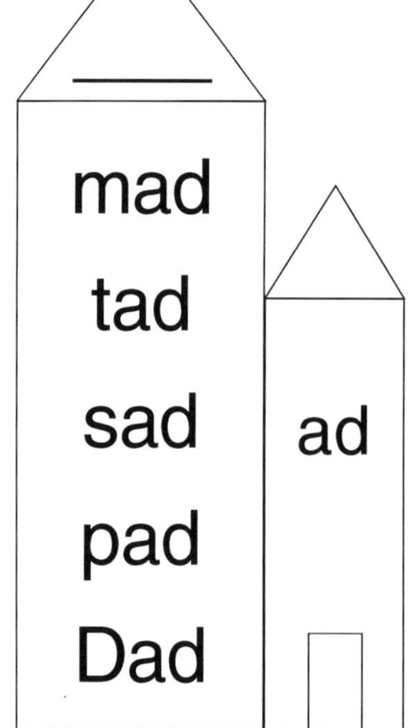

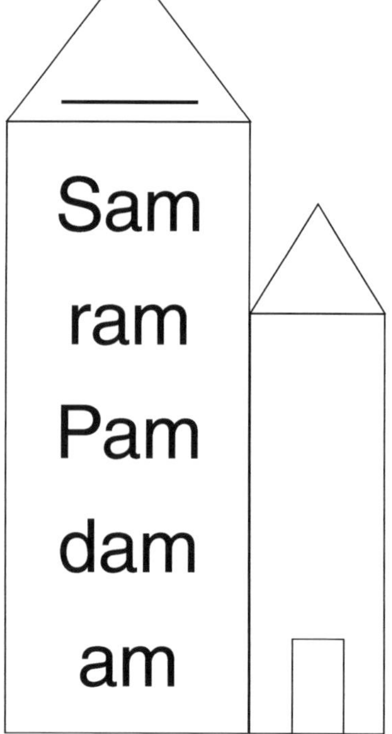

Cut out the words on top and the pictures below. Match the words to the pictures, and glue the pairs on the following page.

cat	mad	can
tag	sad	cap

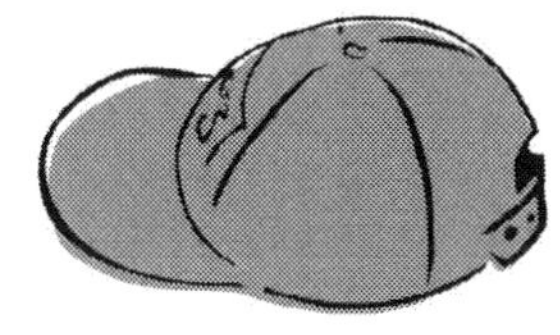		

Reading and writing words.

	nap
	cat
	tag
	cap
	ram
	sad
	sag

you

are

You are my ________________.

You are my ________________.

You are my ________________.

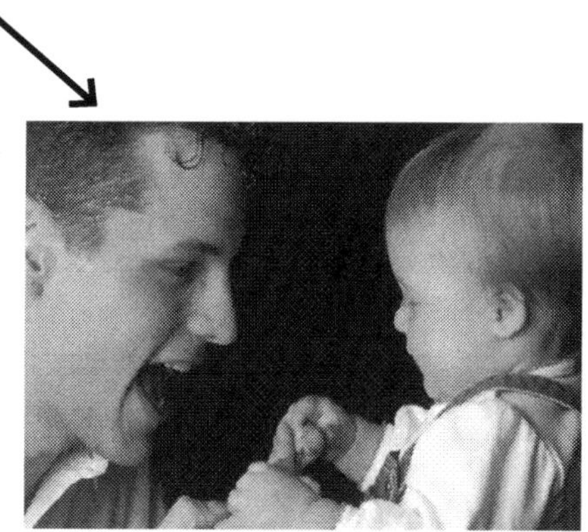

You are my ________________.

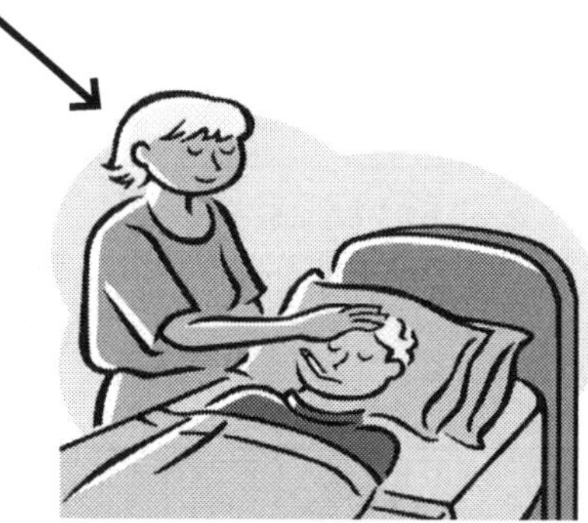

Read the sentence by saying the words and telling about the picture. Draw a circle around the word ***you***. Read the words. Draw a picture of something a child can do. Then draw a circle around the word ***you***.

You can  .

You can  .

You can .

Say the word at the beginning of each row. Draw a circle around the word where you see it in the same row.

that	that	and
you	you	I
are	and	are
my	my	you

Practice Reading

1. gap
2. gag
3. sack
4. tag
5. gas
6. sag
7. mac
8. nag
9. cap
10. can

1. You can tap the cat.
2. You can tap the cat and rat.
3. We can tap you.

1. The man and dad.
2. The man and dad are mad.
3. The man and dad are not mad at you.

Circle three things that belong in the ice cream store.

Read the sentences. Draw a line under the word ***are*** in each sentence.

Are we  ?

Are we  ?

Are we  ?

Are we  .

Say the word at the beginning of each row. Draw a circle around the word where you see it in the same row.

are	are	we
we	we	I
is	are	is
are	I	are

Circle the picture that does ***not belong*** in each group.

Circle the picture that does ***not belong*** in each group.

Circle the picture that does ***not belong*** in each group.

Circle the picture that does ***not belong*** in each group.

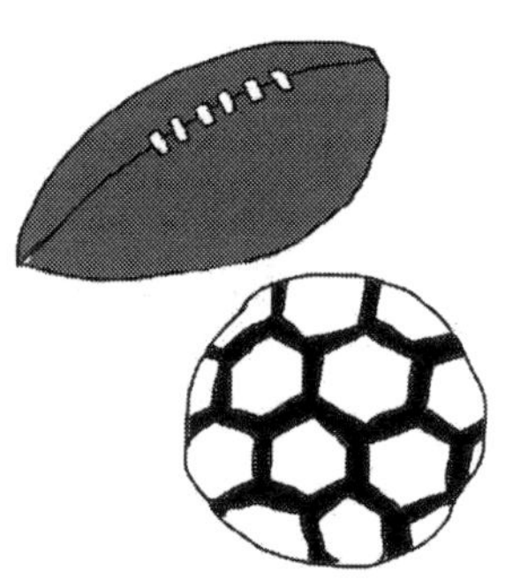

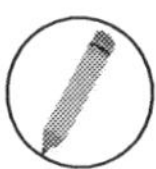

Circle the picture that does ***not belong*** in each group.

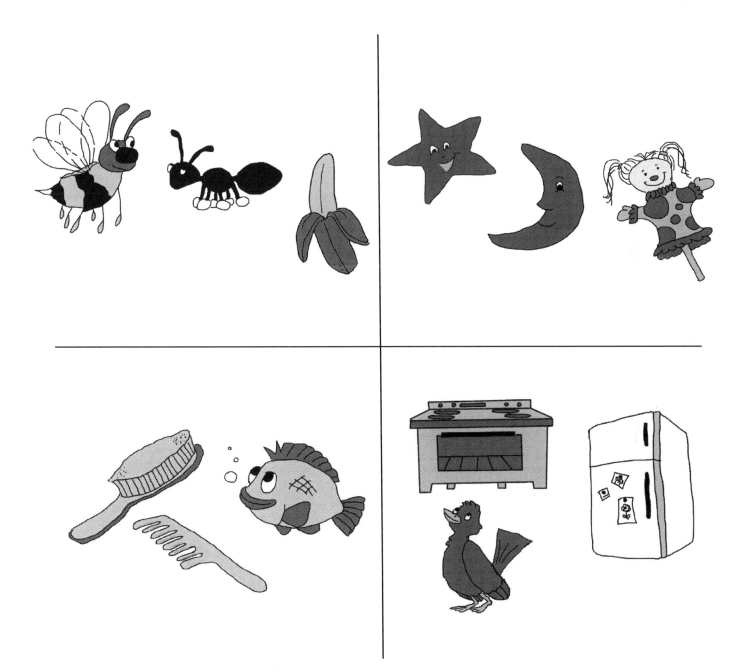

Circle the picture that does ***not belong*** in each group.

Practice the letter ***C***.

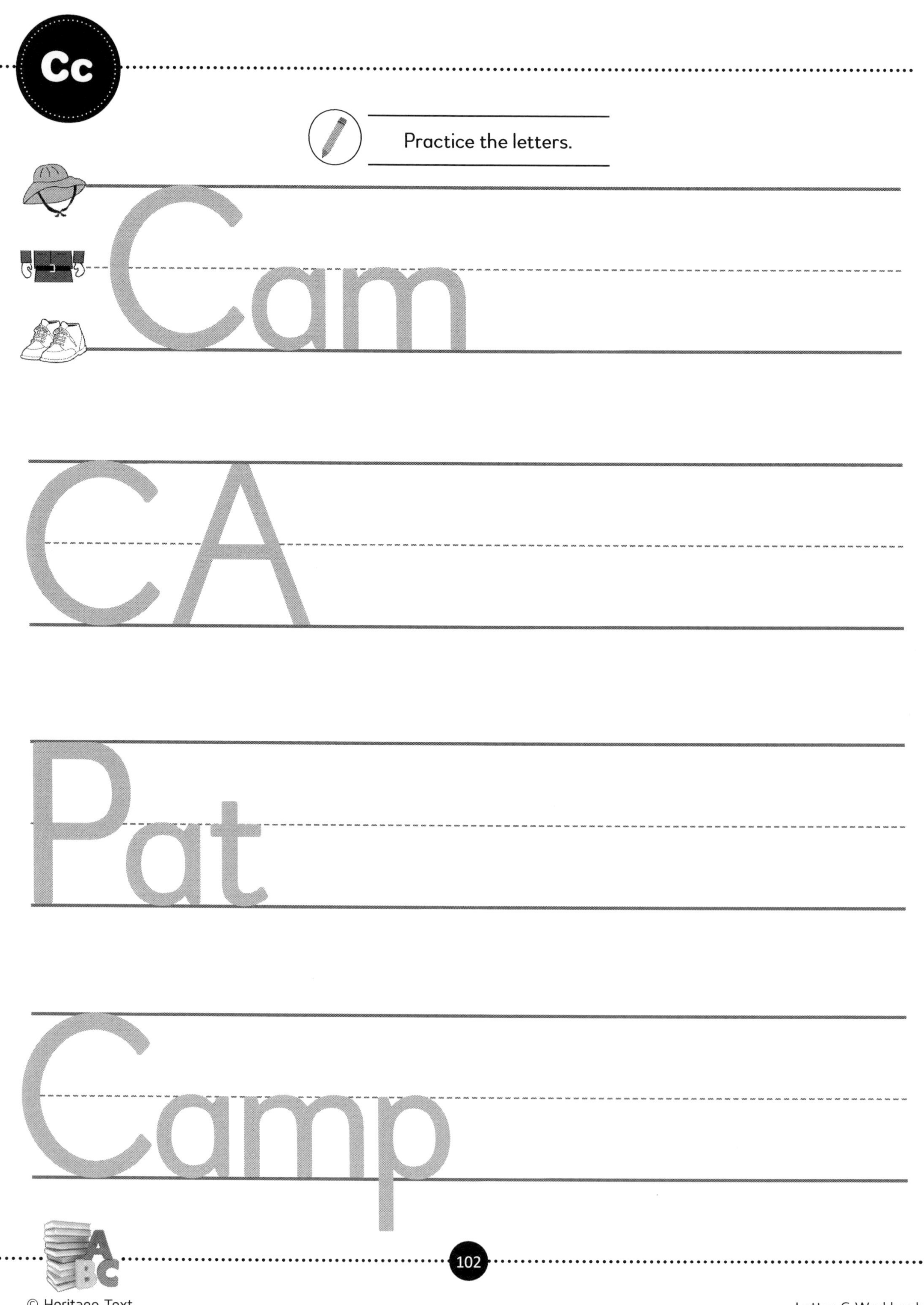
Cc
Practice the letters.
Cam
CA
Pat
Camp

Color the capital **C**s pink. Then color the lowercase **c**s black to reveal a hidden picture.

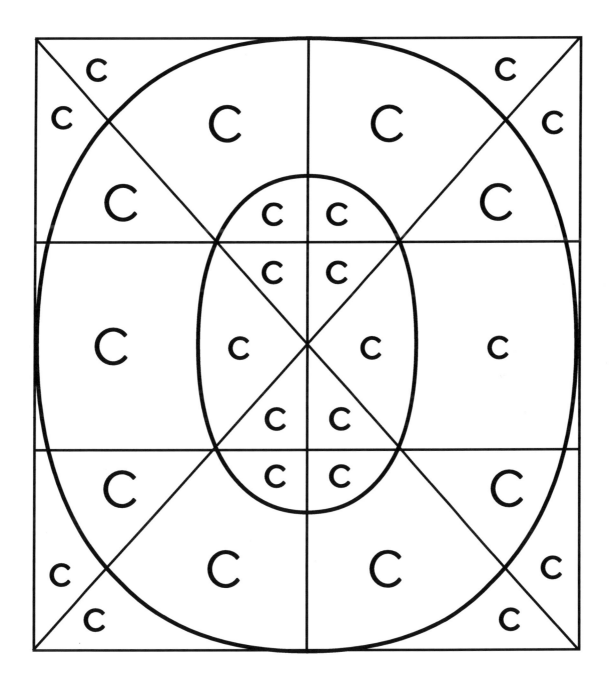

c c
c C C c
C c c C
c c
C c c c
c c
C c c C
c C C c
c c

Draw pictures of words that begin with letter ***h***

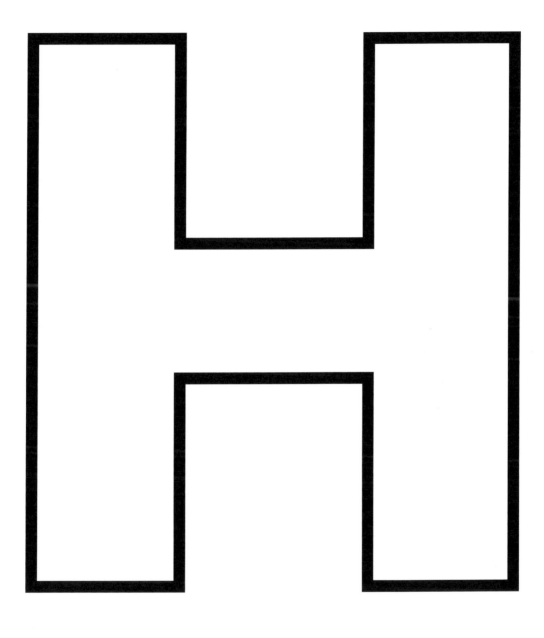

Write the letter ***h***.

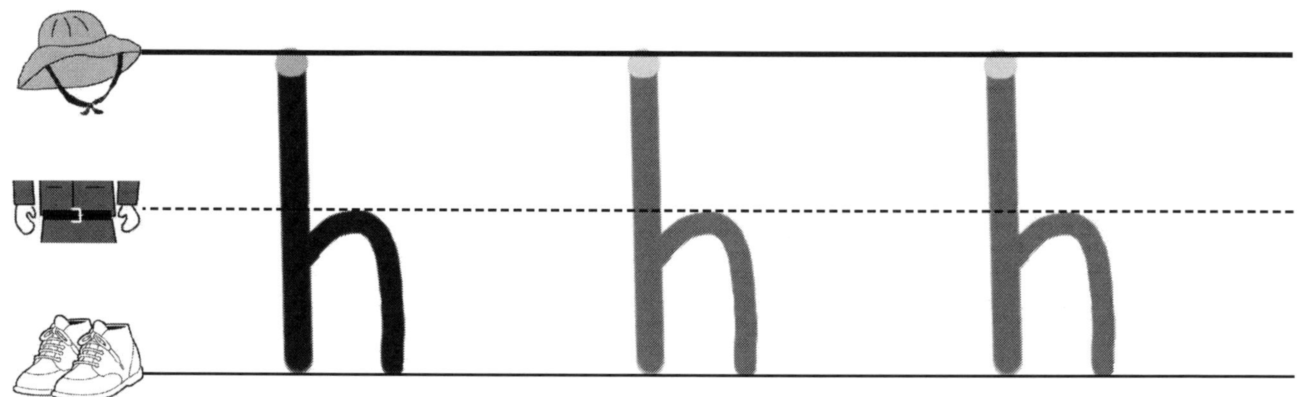

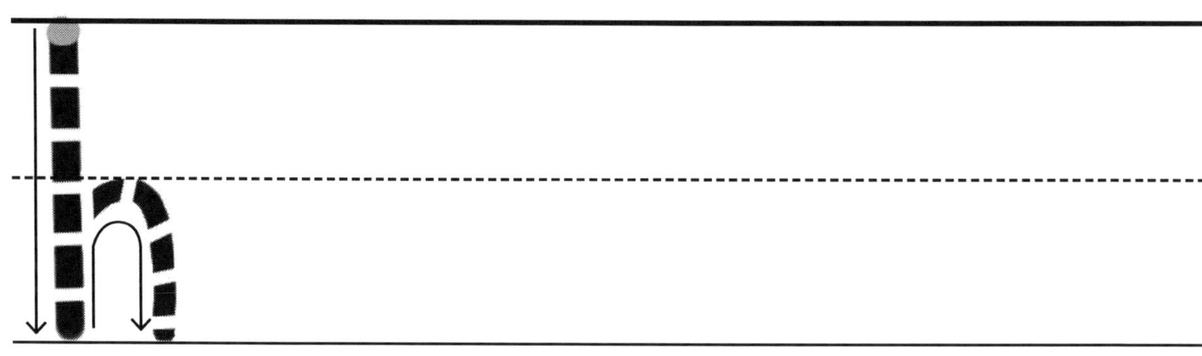

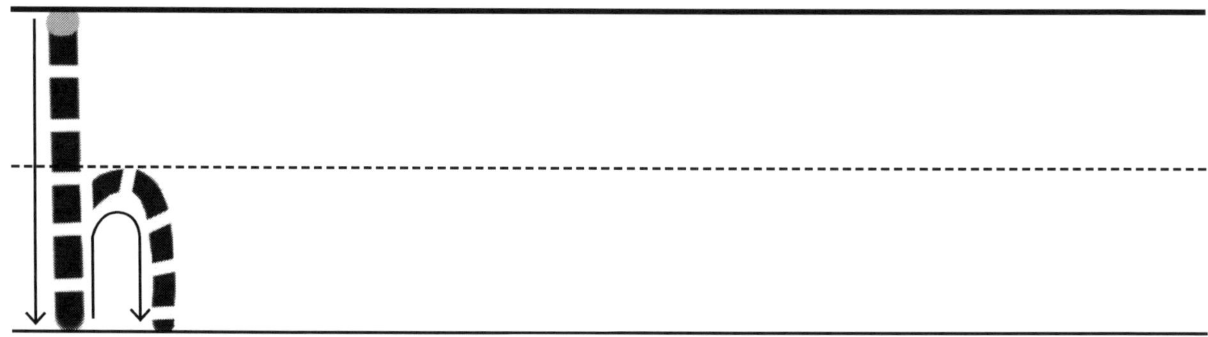

Write the letter ***h***, ***th***, ***ch***, and ***sh***.

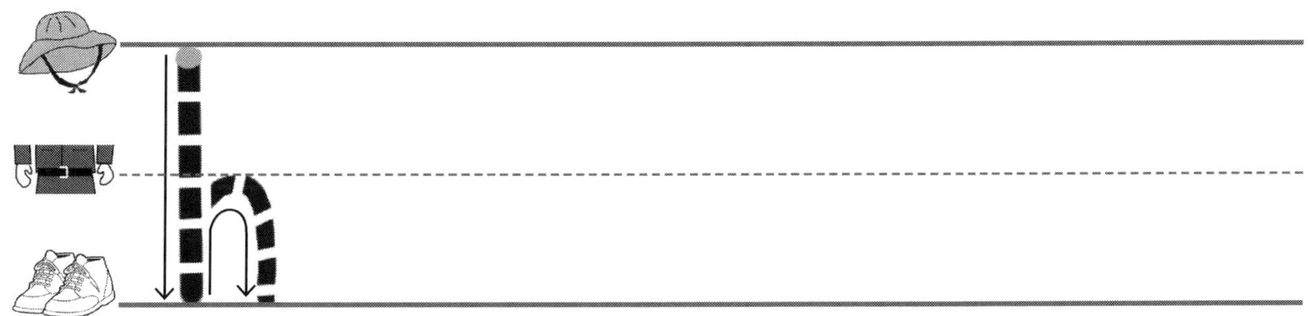

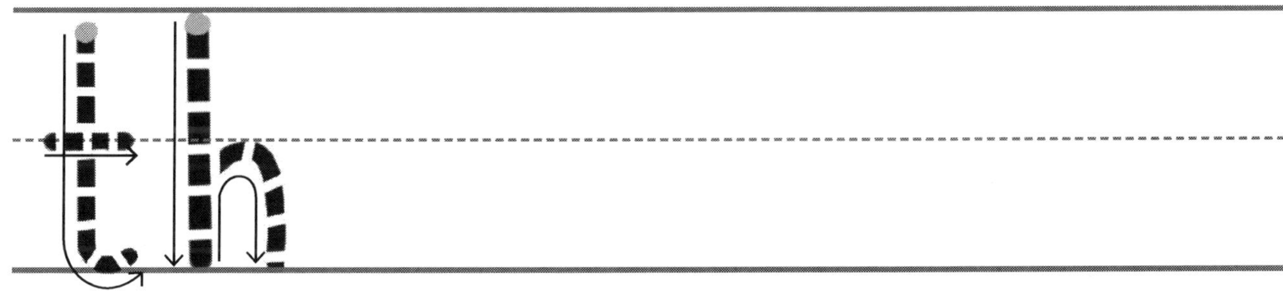

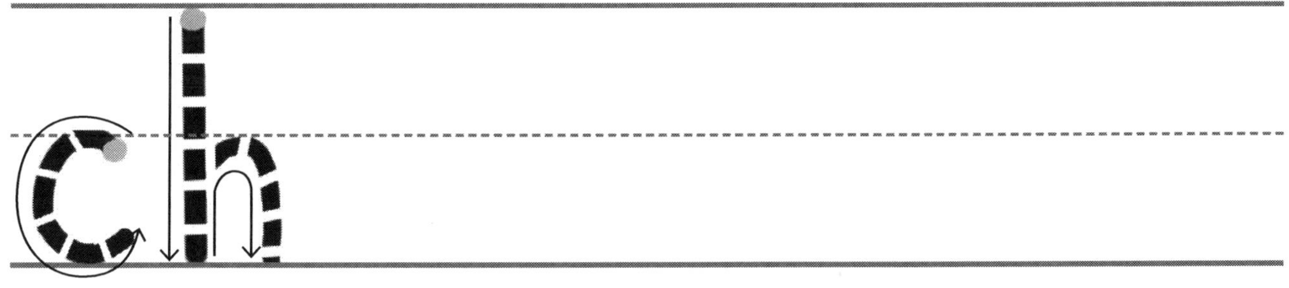

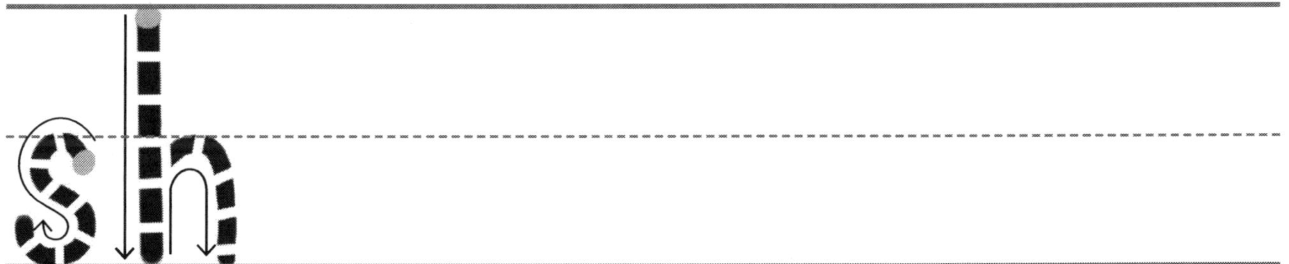

Write the letter ***h***, ***th***, ***ch***, and ***sh***.

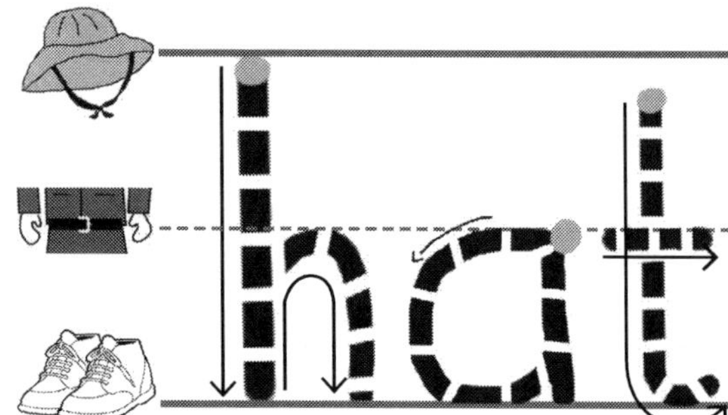

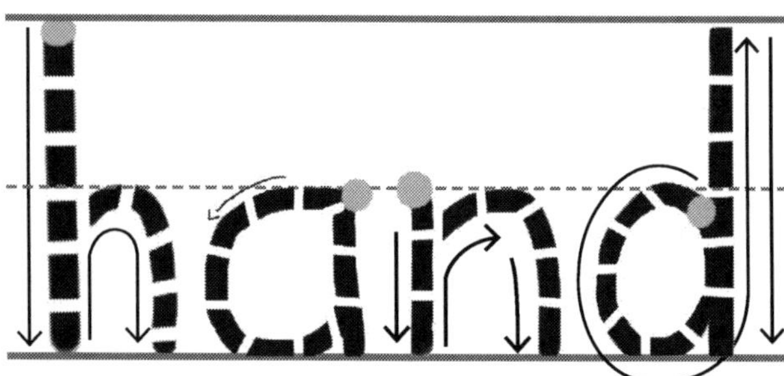

Trace the letter ***Hh***. Say the word that names each picture. Color each picture whos name begins with the same sound as hen. Draw a line from these pictures to the letters ***Hh***.

Name ______________________________

Hh

Name the pictures in each box.
Color each picture that begins with the /**h**/ sound.

1.

2.

 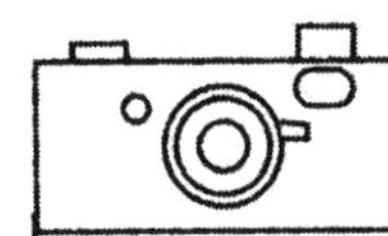

3.

4.

5.

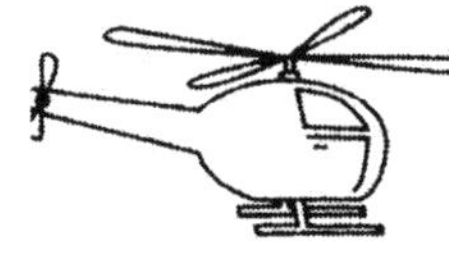 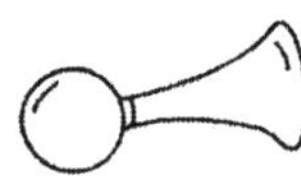

6.

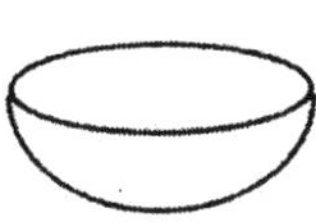 

7.

8.

Write an **h** under each picture whose name begins with the sound ***h***.

1.	2.	3.
4.	5.	6.
7.	8.	9.

Say the picture name. Write the letters that stand for the beginning and ending sound in each picture.

Name ______________________________

1.

h t

2.

3.

4.

Circle the letter that the words begins with.

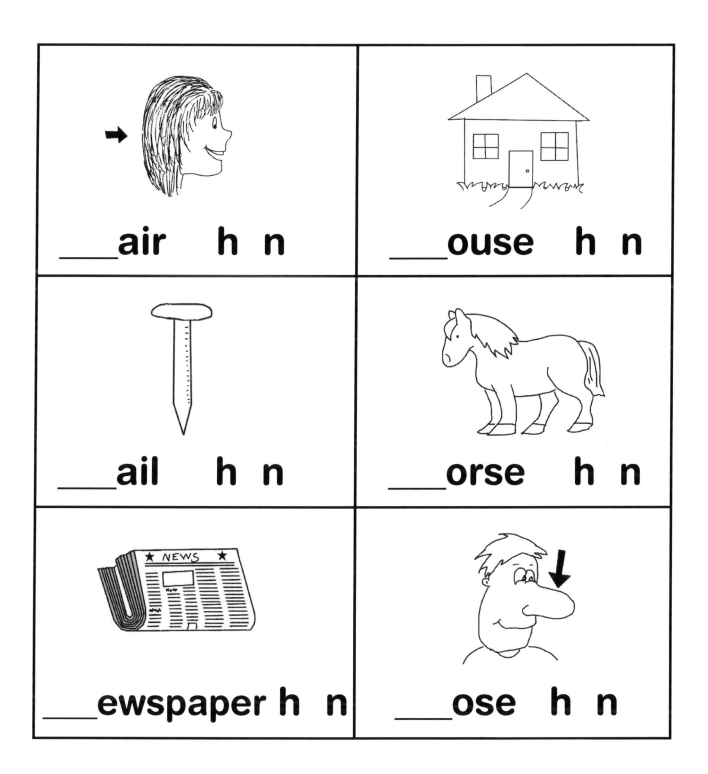

____air h n	____ouse h n
____ail h n	____orse h n
____ewspaper h n	____ose h n

Read the word, tap out the sounds of the word. Then, circle the number of sounds and write the word on the line.

has	 1 2 3 4 5	
had	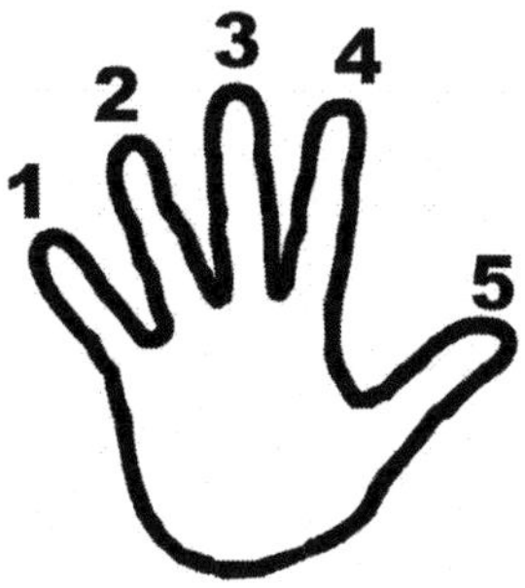 1 2 3 4 5	
	 1 2 3 4 5	
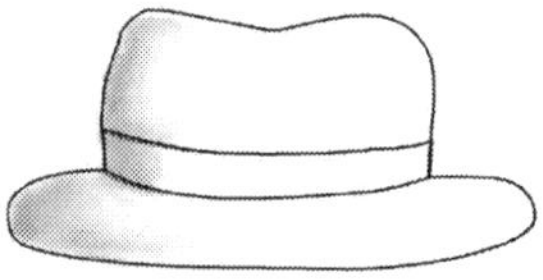	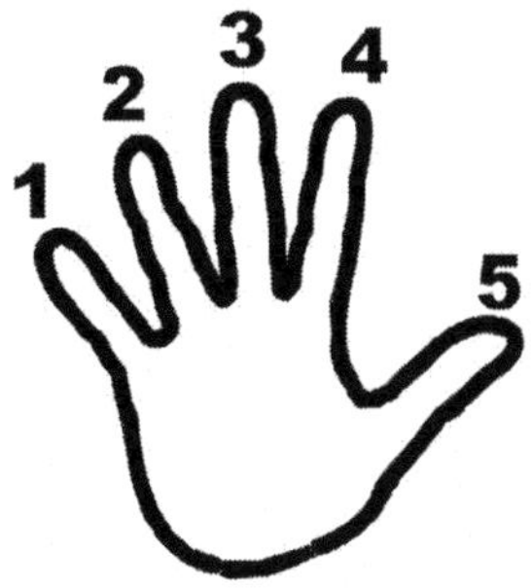 1 2 3 4 5	

Cut out the vowel. Paste it onto a stick. Use the stick to practice blending the vowel before and after each consonant.

a

g
t
h
m
p
s
c

Hh

Cut out the letters on the left. Paste them into the spaces on the right that are missing letters to make words.

Make Words

s	n	t
r	p	t
s	d	t
p	s	n
r	m	d
s	d	n

h	a	
h	a	
h	a	
	a	
	a	
	a	
	a	

Cut out the pictures. Paste them into the correct box.

Name

and 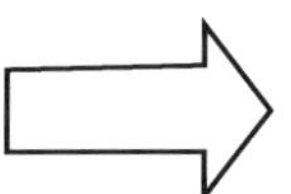	and

h and 	
s and 	

Reading and writing words

	has
	cat
	tag
	cap
	ham
	had
	hat

his

has

red

his

his

his

Ann has a

Dan has a

Nan has a ___________

Read the sight word at the beginning of each row. Circle the same sight word in the row.

Sight Words

his	his	has	is
has	his	has	had
red	had	red	ram

Read.

Sam has a red hat.

You had a nap on the mat.

Nan said that is not a rat. It is a cat.

Read the phrases below. Use a red crayon to draw a picture depicting the phrase.

1. the red hat	
2. on the red mat	
3. a red hat for you	
4. his red cap	

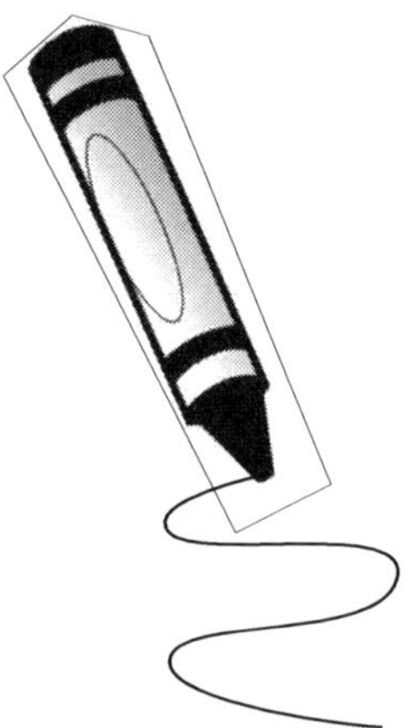

Circle two pictures that make a ***pair***.

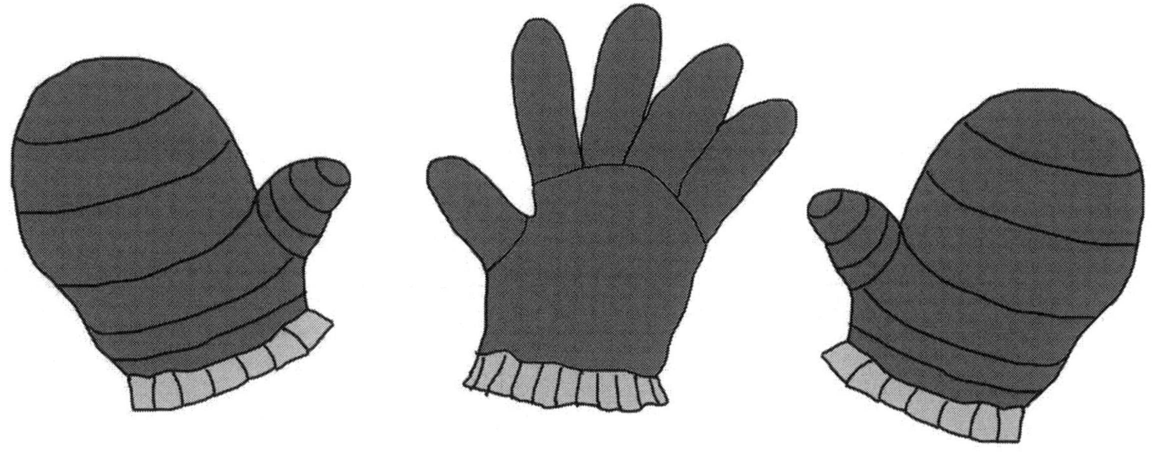

Circle two pictures that make a ***pair***.

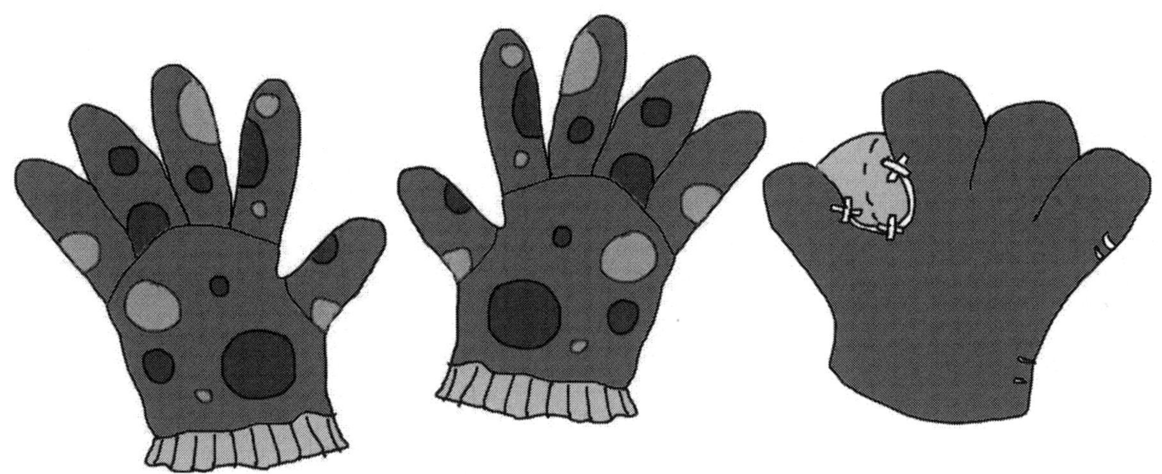

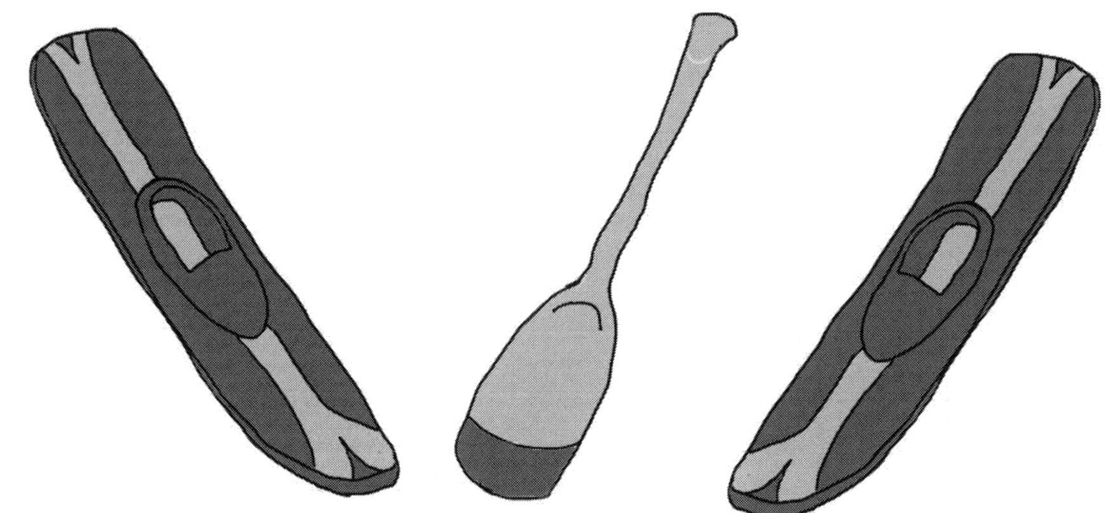

Circle two pictures that make a ***pair***.

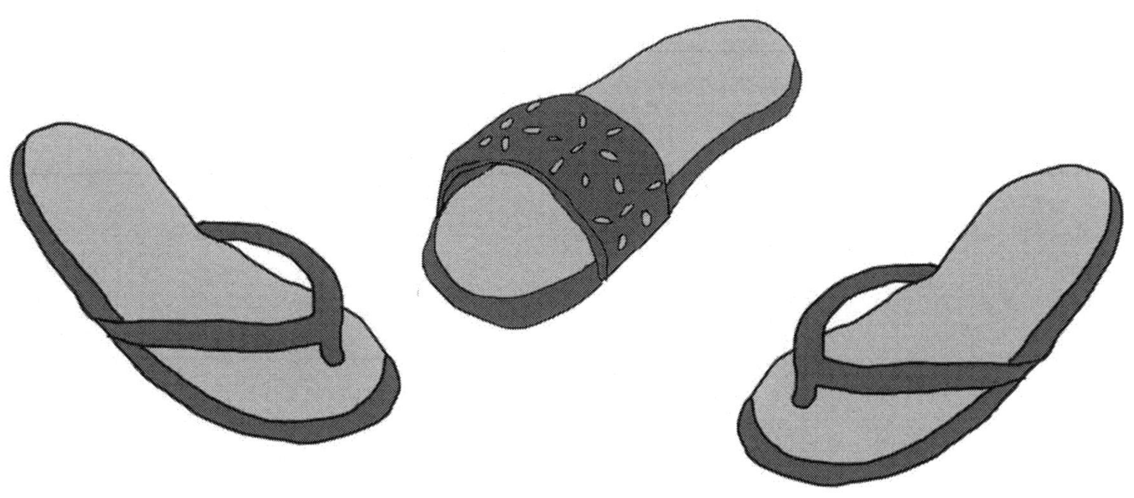

Circle two pictures that make a ***pair***.

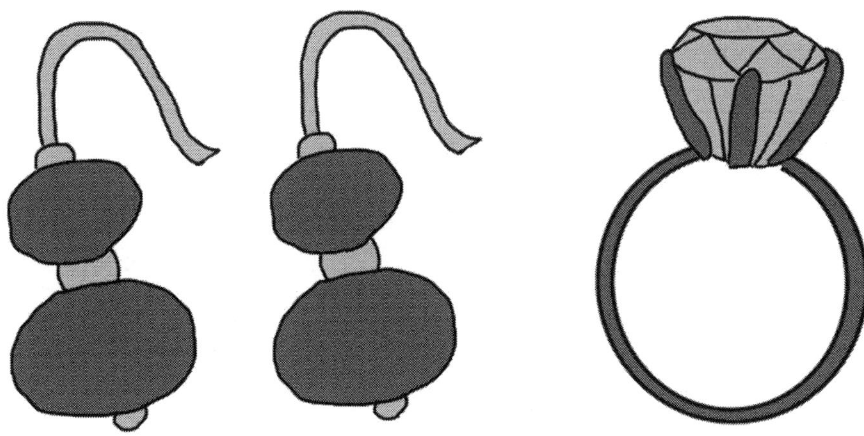

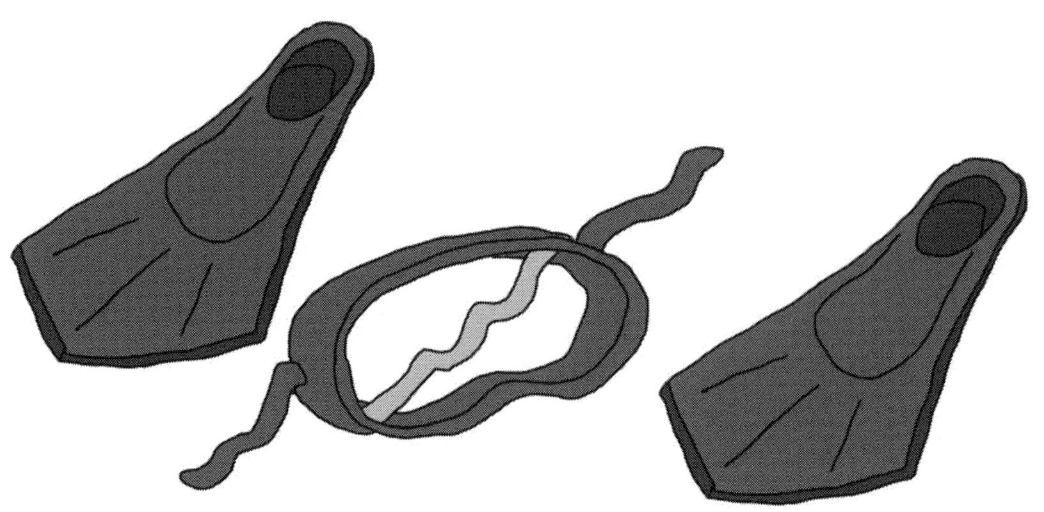

Draw pictures of words that begin with letter ***f***

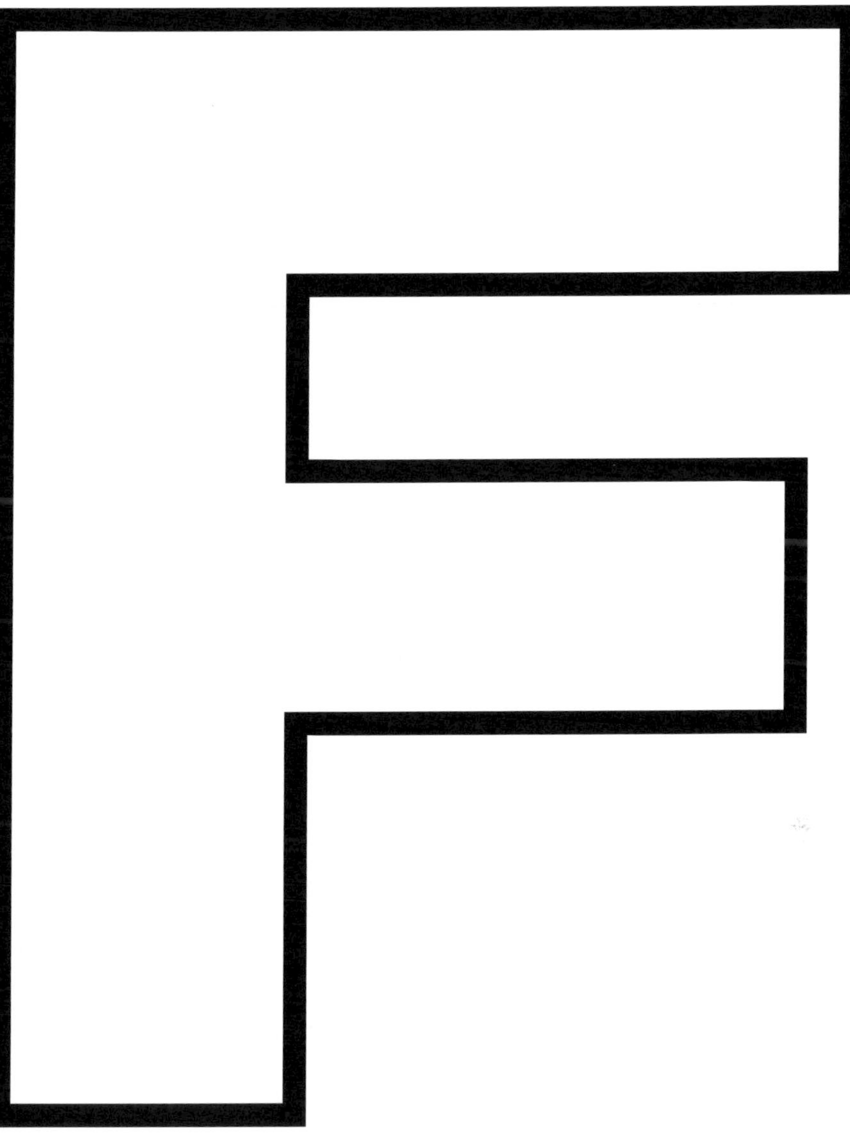

Write the letter ***f***.

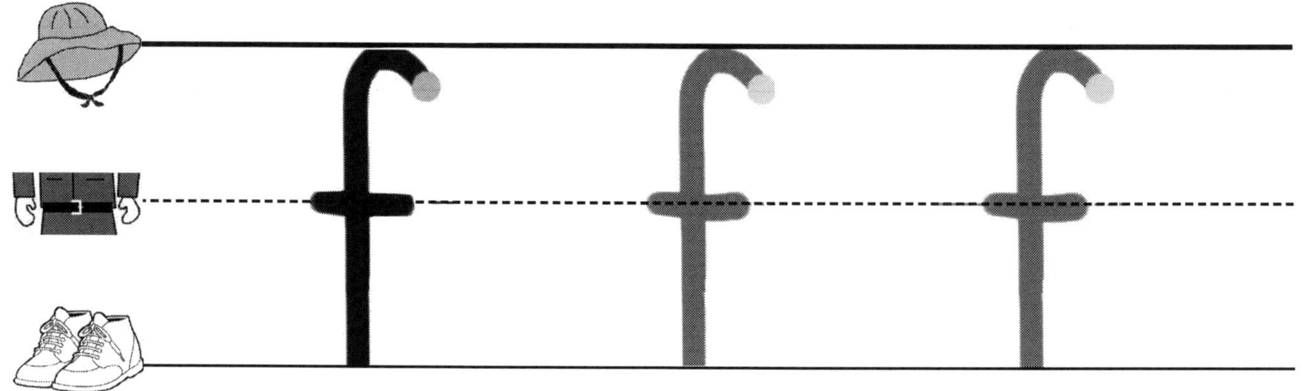

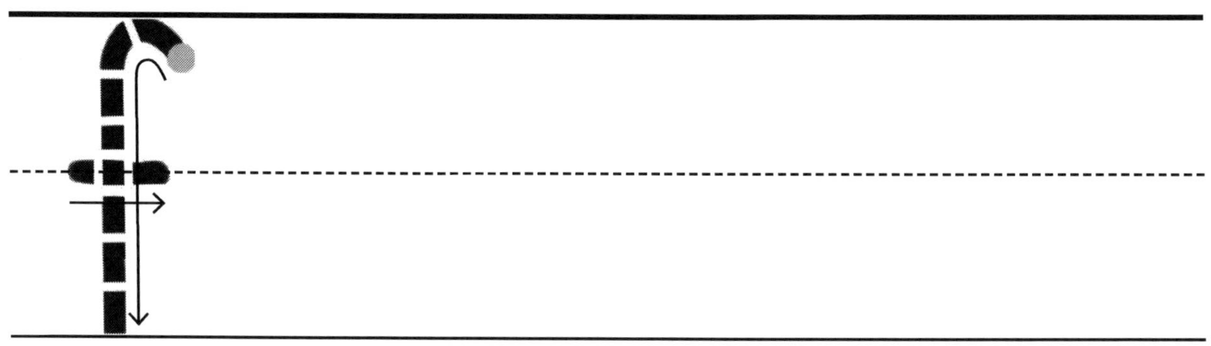

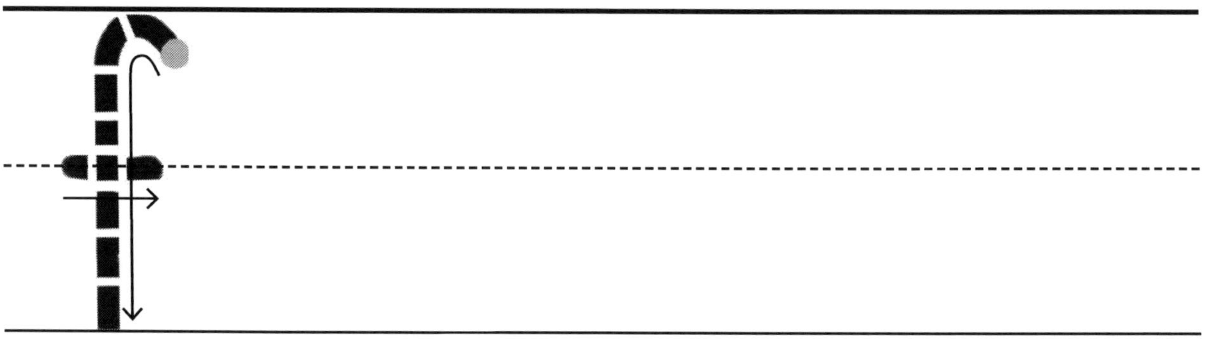

Write the letter ***f***, ***h***, ***c***, and ***g***.

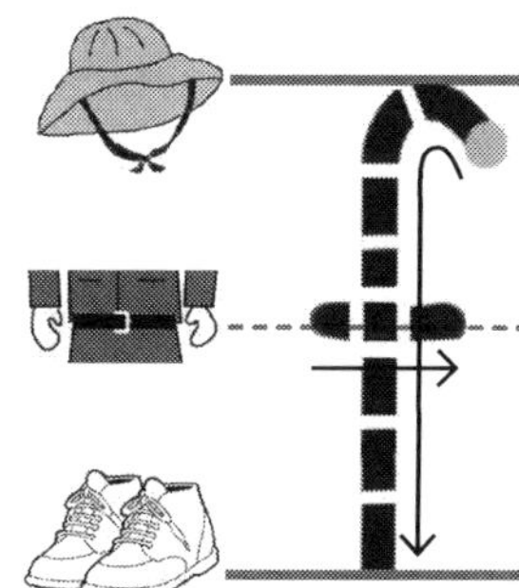

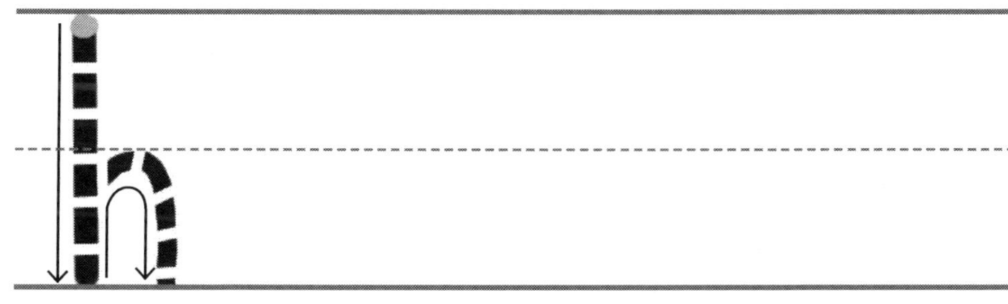

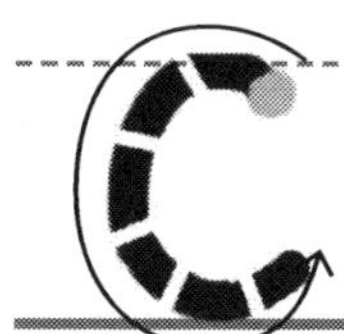

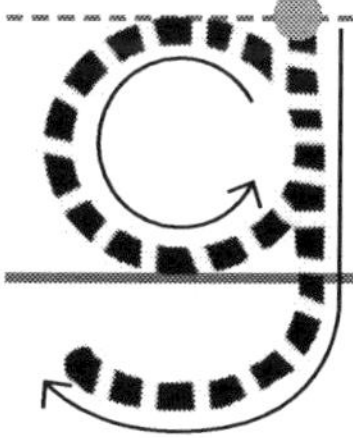

Ff

Write the letters ***fr***, ***fan***, ***fad***, and ***fast***.

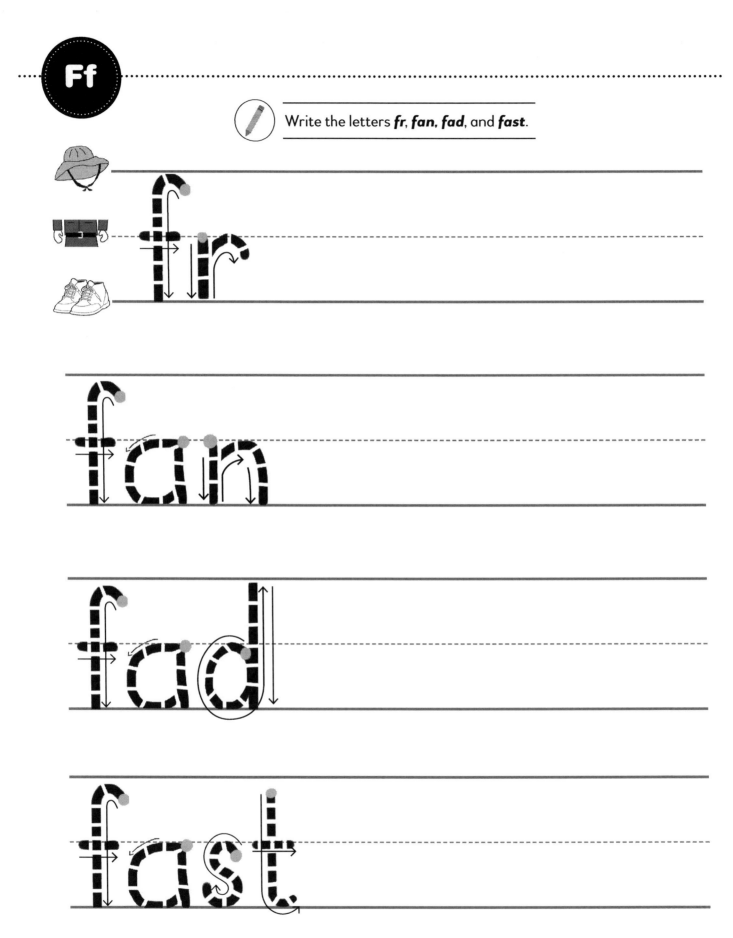

fr

fan

fad

fast

Write the words ***fact*** and ***raft***.

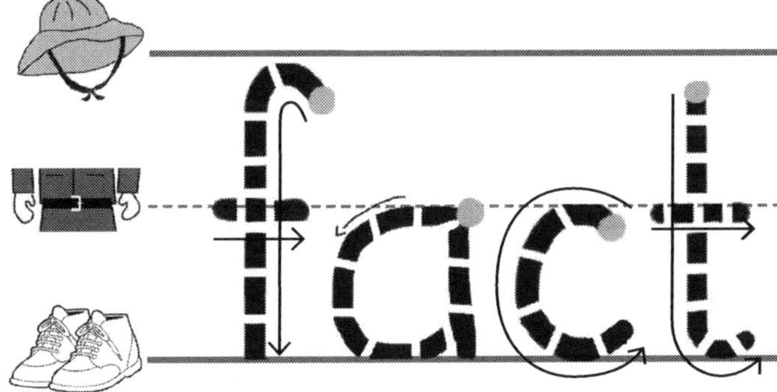

Trace the letter ***Ff***. Say the word that names each picture. Color each picture whos name begins with the same sound as fish. Draw a line from these pictures to the letter ***Ff***.

Name ______________________________

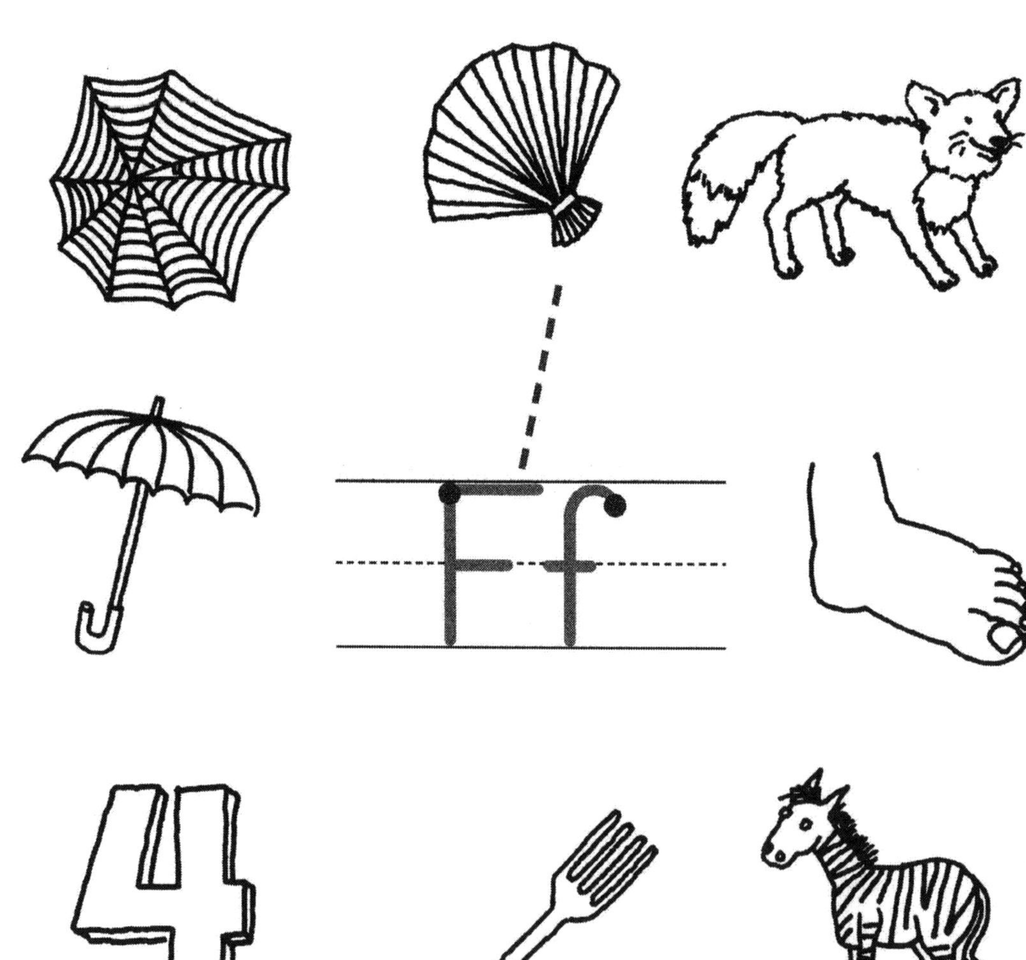

Point to the **feather** in the corner and say its name.
Find pictures in the scene that start the same as feather.
Color the pictures that start like **feather**.

Ff

Name the pictures on the page.
Circle the picture if it **ends** like leaf.

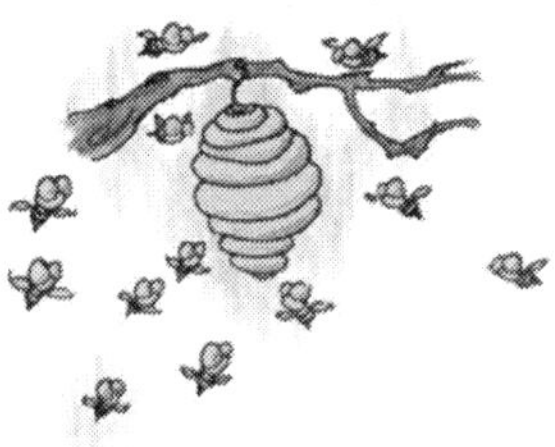

Name the pictures on this page. Circle the first ***f*** it if begins like ***fish***, and circle the second ***f*** if it ends like ***leaf***.

Name ____________________

 f f	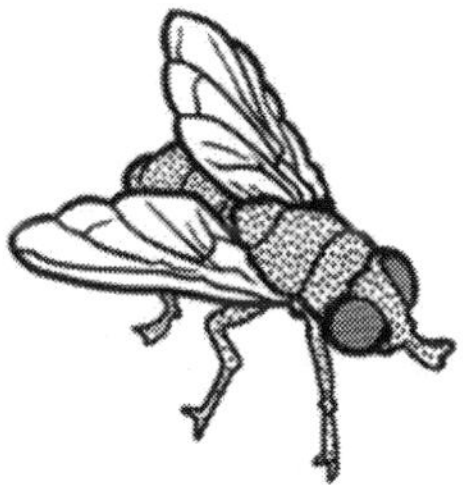 f f	 f f
 f f	 f f	 f f
 f f	 f f	 f f

Circle the correct letter that the words begins with.

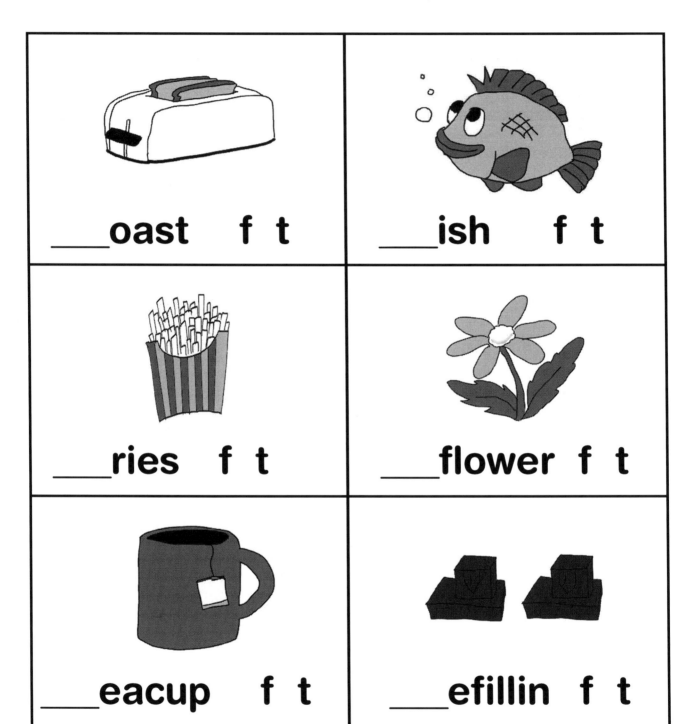

___oast f t	___ish f t
___ries f t	___flower f t
___eacup f t	___efillin f t

Say the name of each picture. Draw a circle around the letter that stands for the **sound** you hear at the **beginning** of each picture.

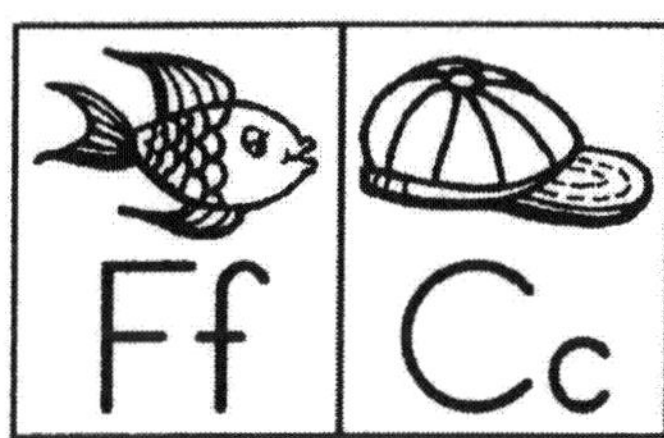

Name ____________________

f c	f c
f c	f c
f c	f c

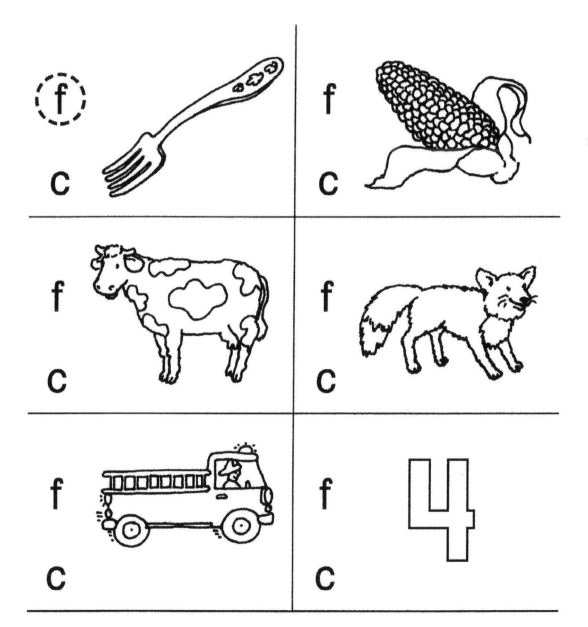

Look at the letter at the beginning of the row. Color the picture whos name begins with the sound the letter stands for.

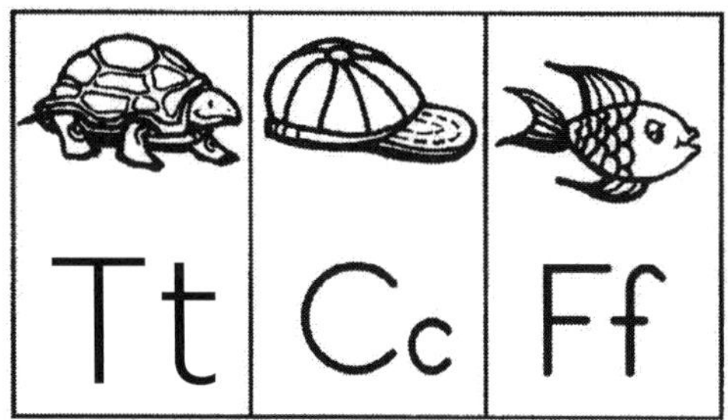

Name ____________________

Tt	
Cc	
Ff	

Say the name of each picture. Draw a circle around the letter that stands for the sound you hear at the **beginning** of each picture name. Say the name of each picture. Draw a circle around the letter that stands for the sound you hear at the **end** of each picture name.

Name ______________________________

c t f	c t f
c t f	c t f
c t f	c t f

Read the words in each house. Fill in the name of the **family** in the roof. Then help the lost words in the gray box to find their home.

hat
hand
tag
fan
fad
had
ham

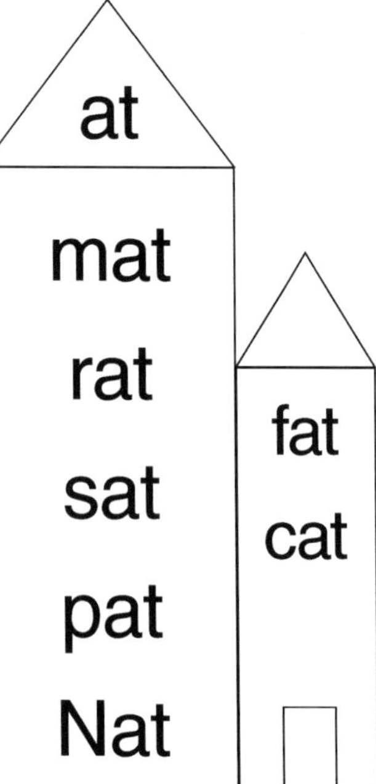

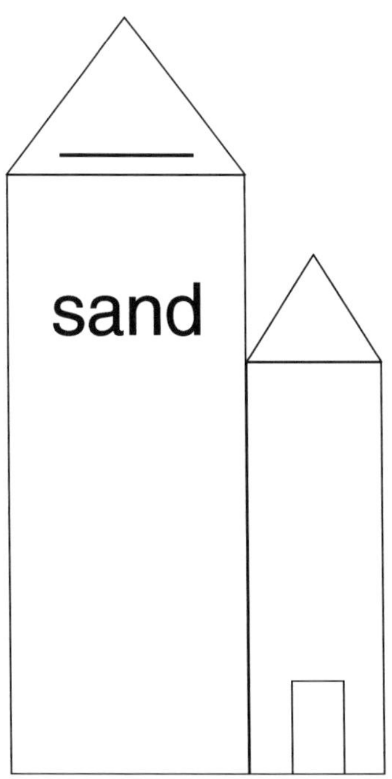

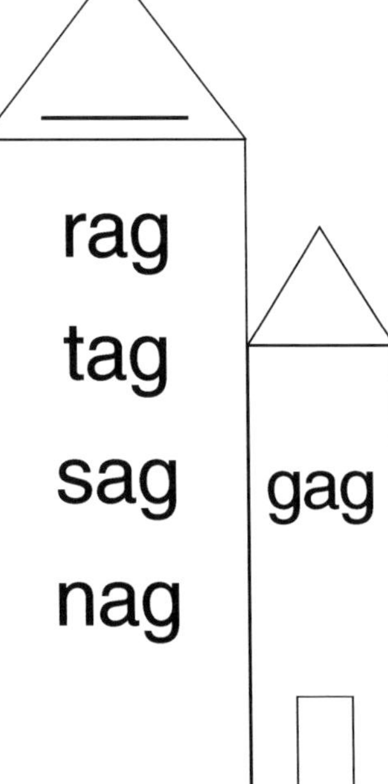

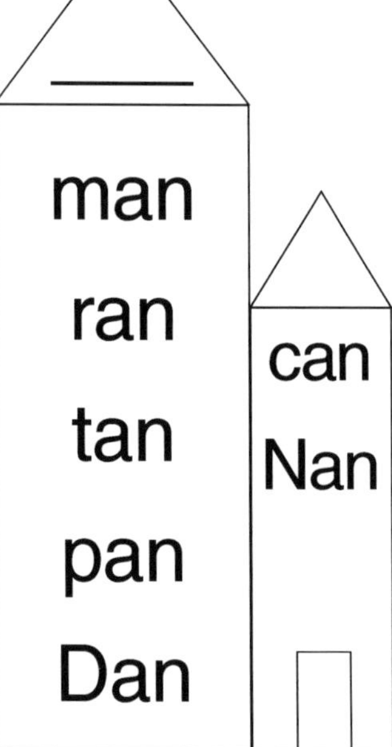

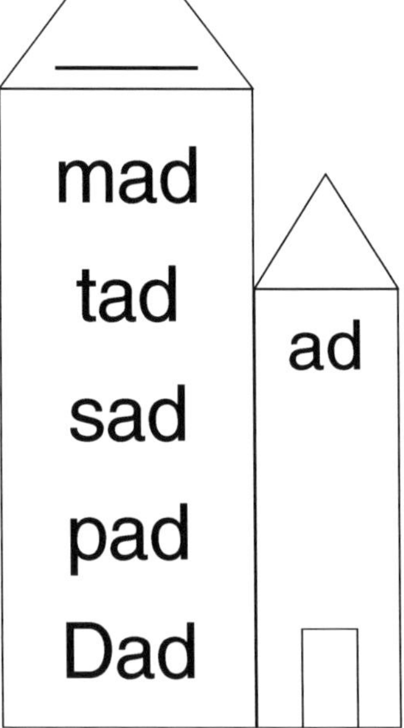

Sam
ram
Pam
dam
am

Cut out the letters on the left. Paste them into the spaces on the right that are **missing letters** to make words.

Make Words

s	n	t
r	p	t
s	d	t
p	s	n
r	m	d
s	d	n

f	a	
f	a	
	a	
	a	
	a	
	a	
	a	

Cut out the **vowel**. Paste it onto a stick. Use the stick to practice blending the vowel **before** and **after** each consonant.

Name ______________________________

a

______	g	______
______	t	______
______	h	______
______	f	______
______	p	______
______	s	______
	c	

Read the words and sentences.
Then, draw a picture in the box.

Name

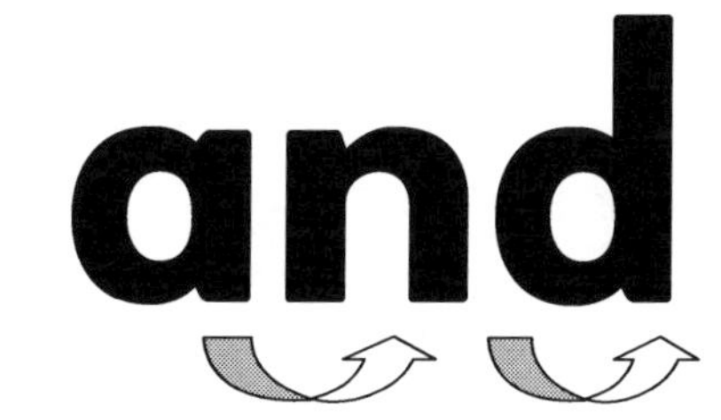

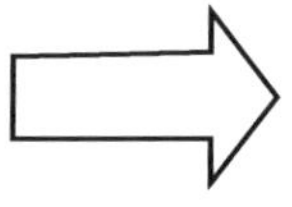

and

h and	My <u>hand</u> is like a fan.
s and	The fat cat is in the <u>sand</u>.

Reading and writing words

	has
	fad
	tag
	cap
	fan
	hand
	fat

with

no

for

 Match the foods that go together.

 with 

 with 

 with 

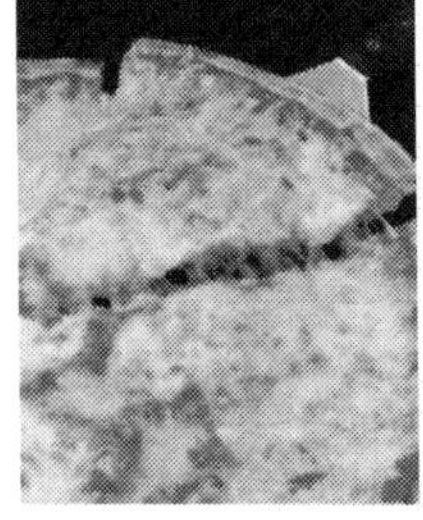 with 

Read the phrases to find out what you are **not** allowed to do!

no 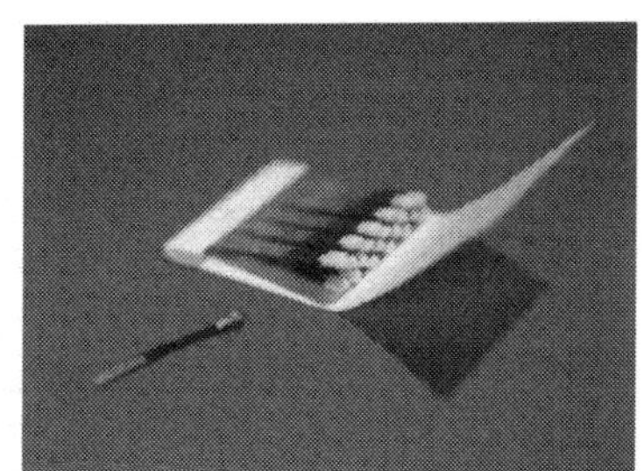

no 

no 

Match the foods that go together.

 for 

 for 

 for 

for

Read the sight word at the **beginning** of each row.
Circle the **same** sight word you find in the row.

Sight Words

with	the	that	with
no	no	on	in
for	like	we	for

Circle the sight words;

with	fan	fat	cat	hat
had	has	his	hand	
sand	fad	no	ham	
hap	Sam			

Practice reading

1. has	6. fad
2. fan	7. had
3. fat	8. hack
4. ham	9. hap
5. hat	10. Han

1. Are you with my dad?
2. No I am not with dad.
3. I am with the fat cat.
4. I am with the fat cat on the mat.
5. We like to nap on the mat.

1. The fan is on.
2. The fan is on for you.

Read the sentences below.
Draw a picture about the sentence.

Sam has a red cap and a bat. Sam is sad.

Sam has a red cap and a fan. Sam is not sad.

Read the sentences below.
Draw a picture about the sentence.

Sam has a fat cat.

Sam and the fat cat nap.

I like Sam.

Match the picture of each mother to her baby. Color the pictures.

Color the pictures in each row that go together.
Write an **X** on the one that does ***not*** belong.

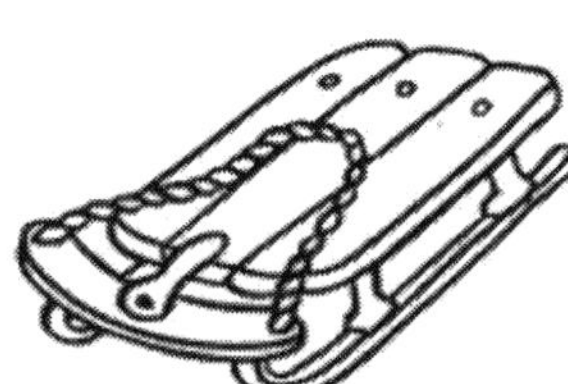

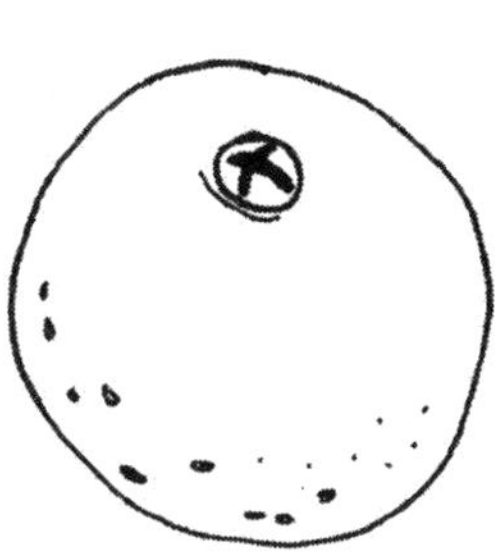

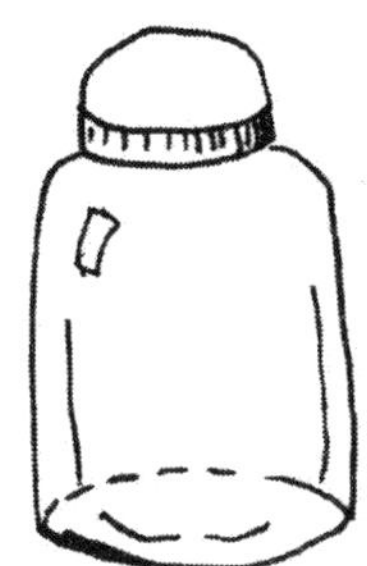

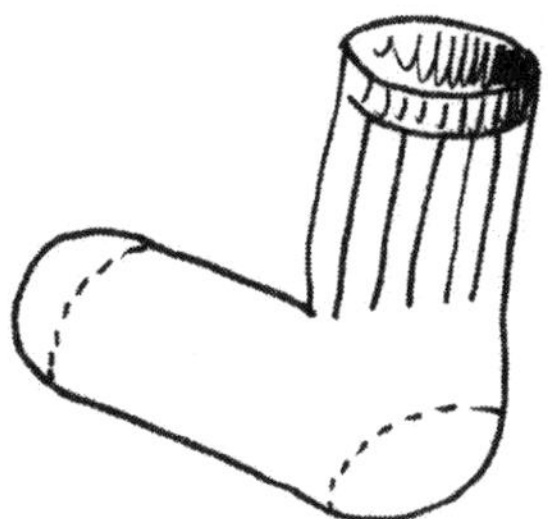
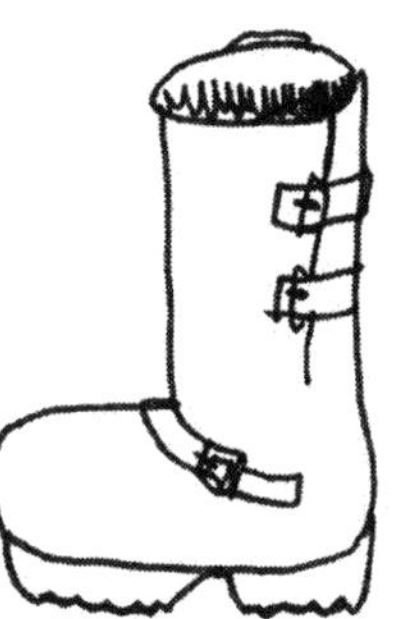

Circle the picture that belongs with the **first** picture in each row.

Circle the picture that belongs with the **first** picture in each row.

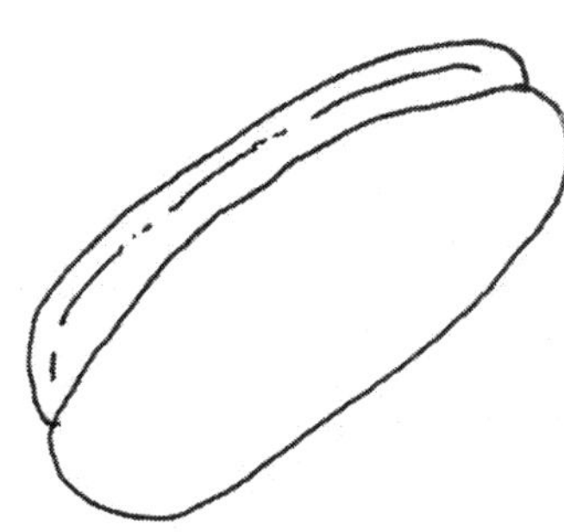

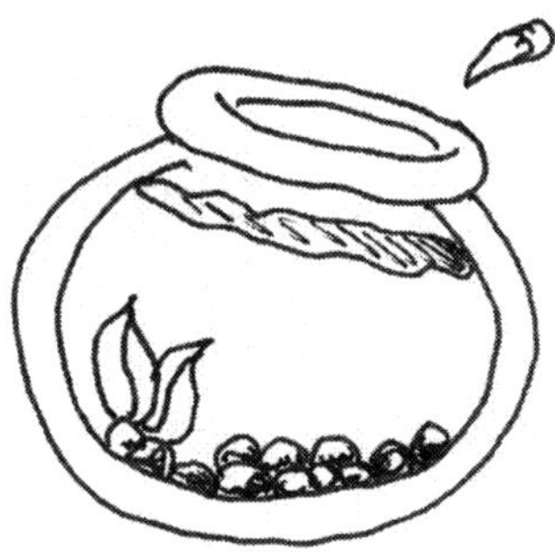

Circle the picture that belongs with the **first** picture in each row.

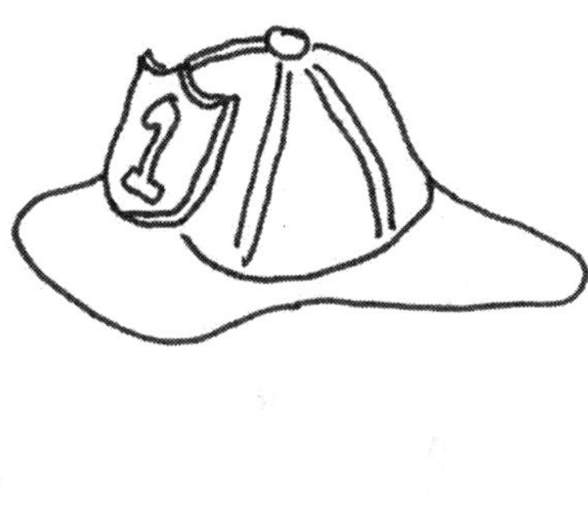

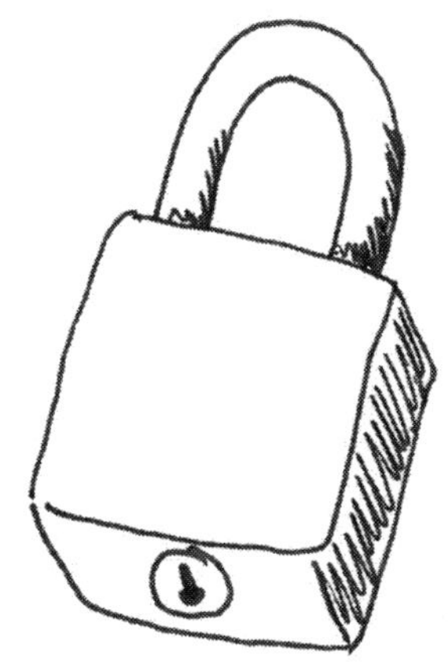

Circle the picture that belongs with the **first** picture in each row.

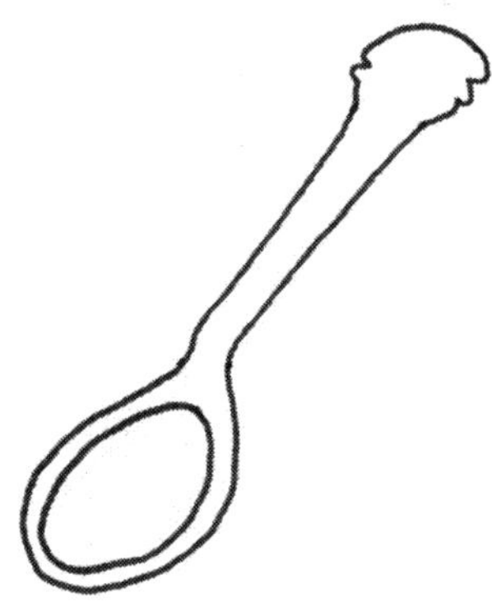

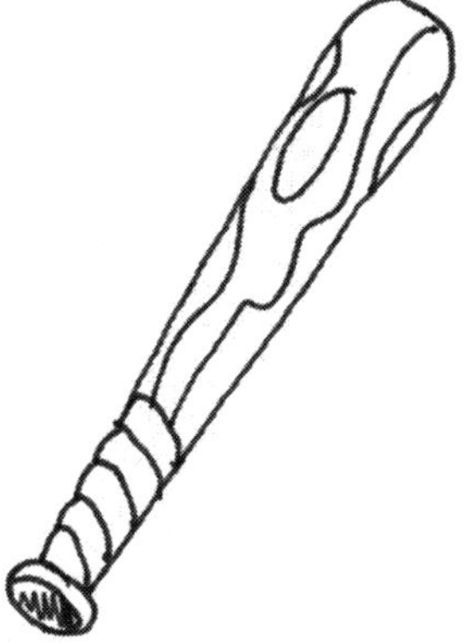

Circle the picture that belongs with the **first** picture in each row.

Practice the letter ***F***.

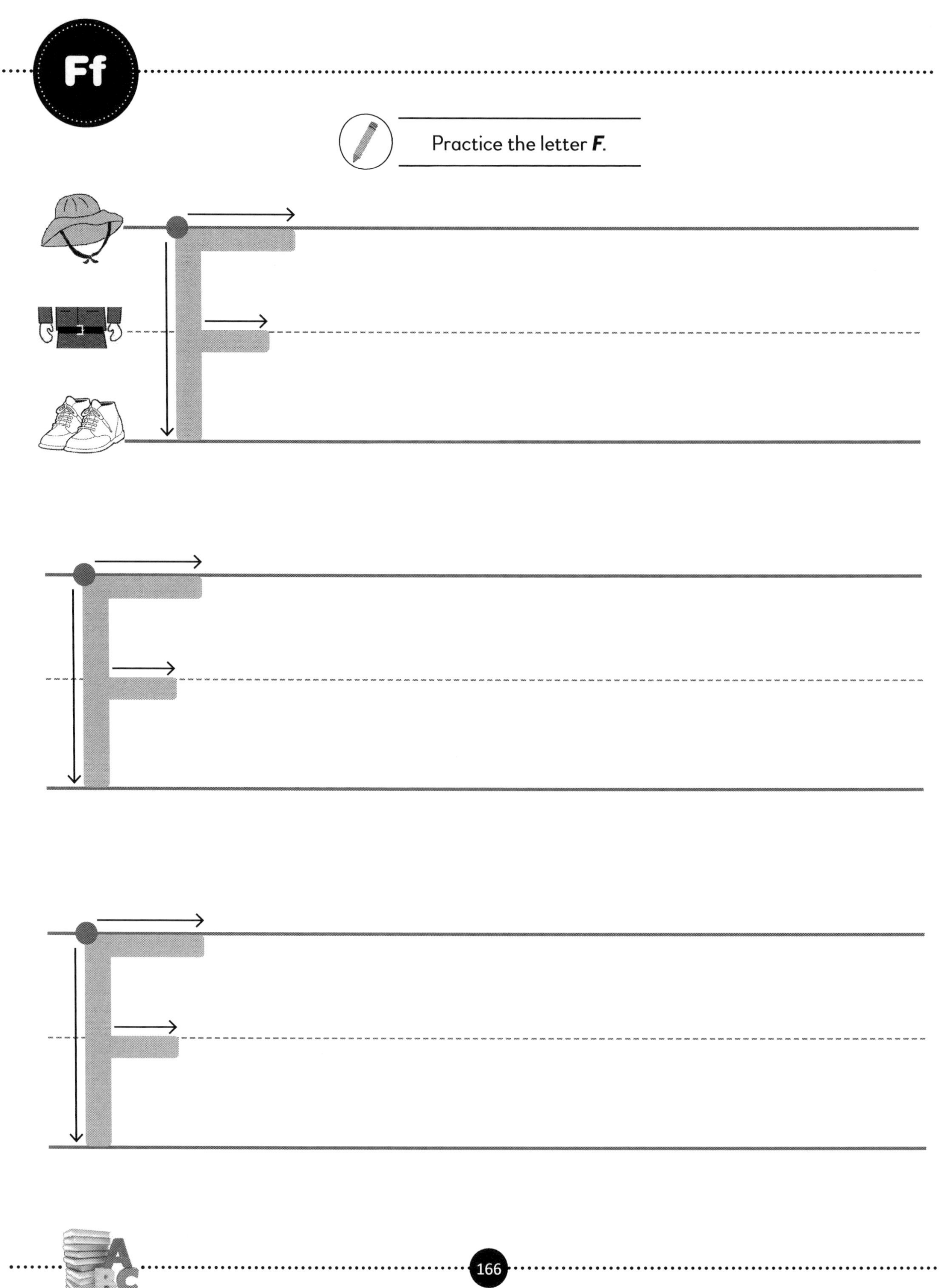

Practice the letters.

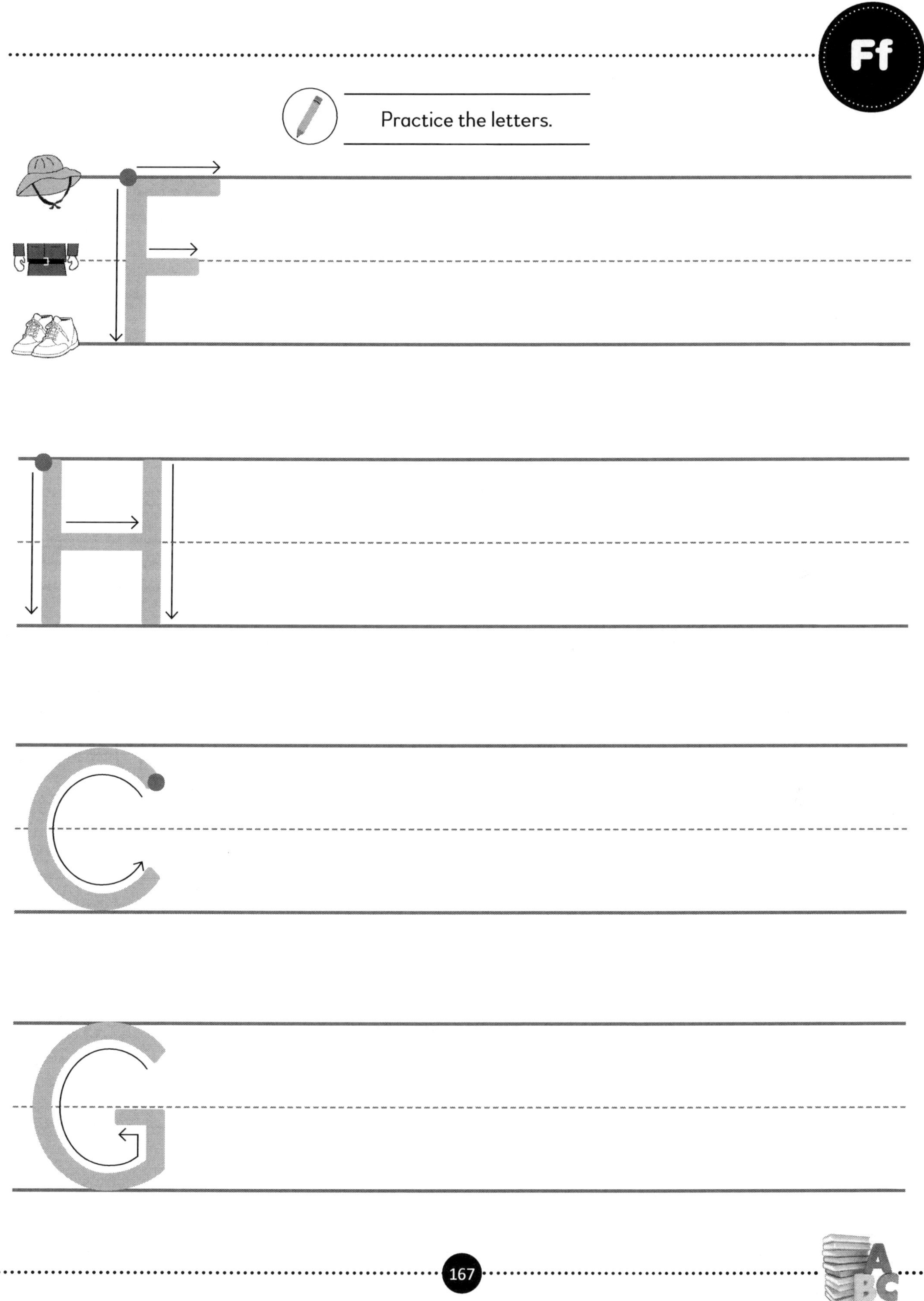

Color the capital ***F's*** green. Color the lower case ***f's*** grey.

F	f	f	f	f	F
F	f	F	F	F	F
F	f	f	f	F	F
F	f	F	F	F	F
F	f	F	F	F	F

Draw pictures of words that begin with letter ***k***

K

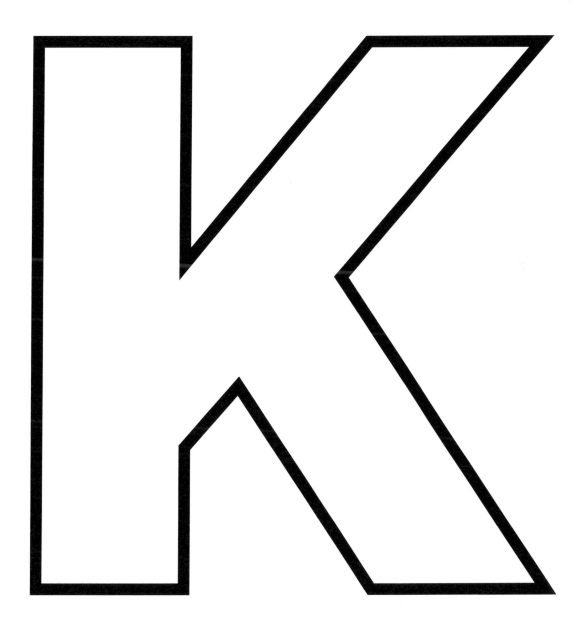

Write the letter ***k***

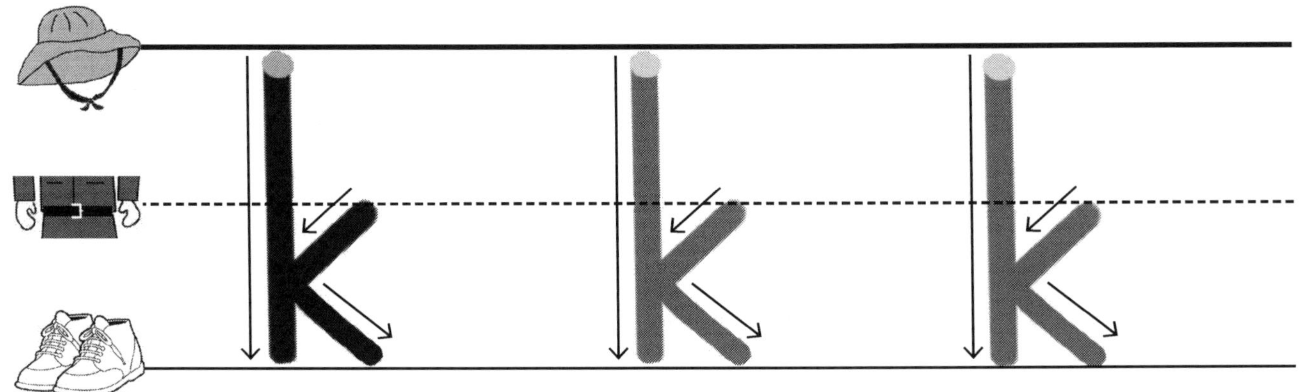

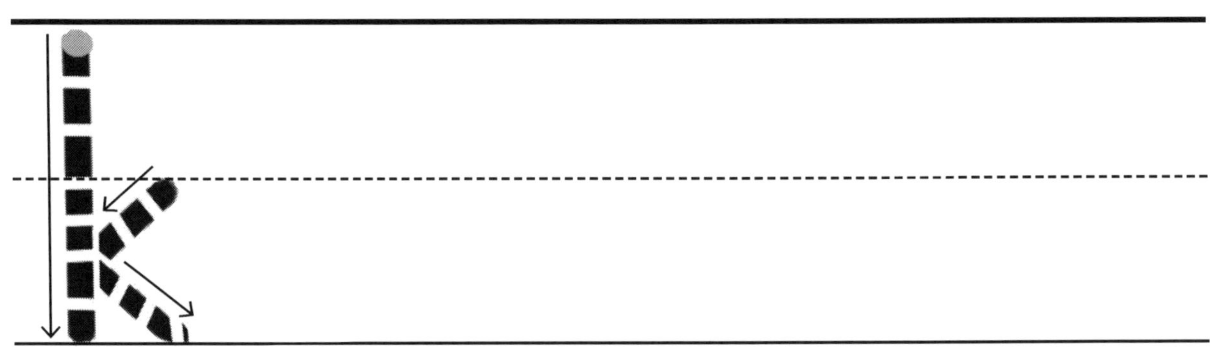

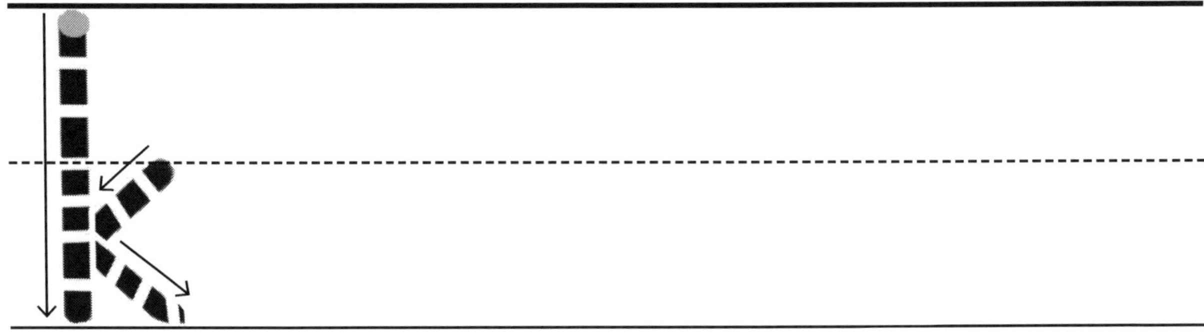

Write the letter ***k***, ***f***, ***ck***, and ***nk***.

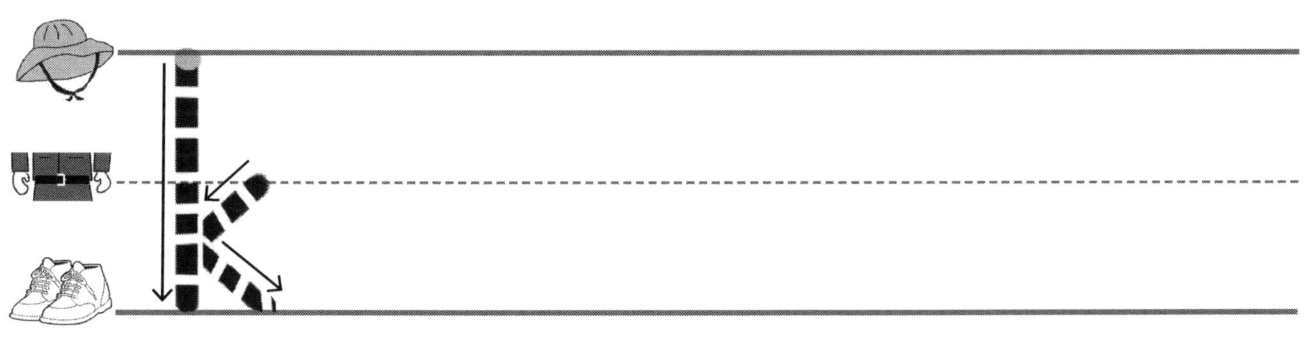

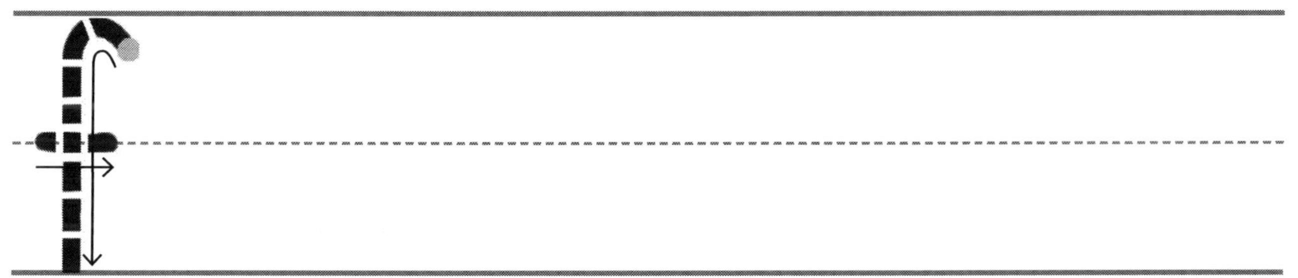

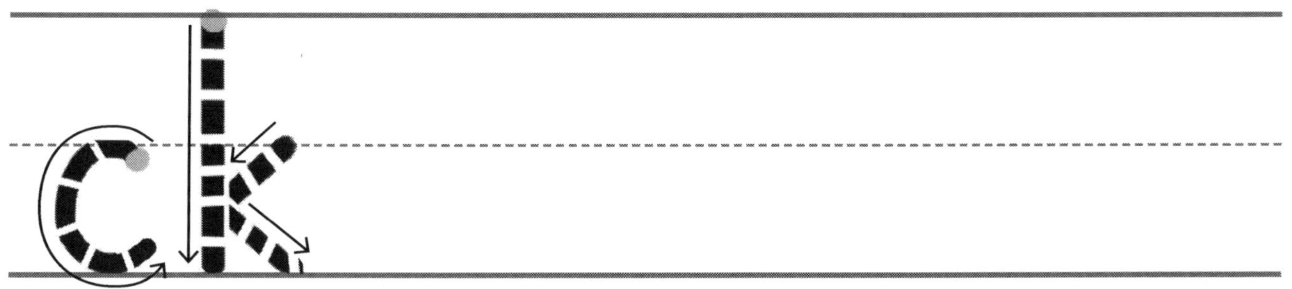

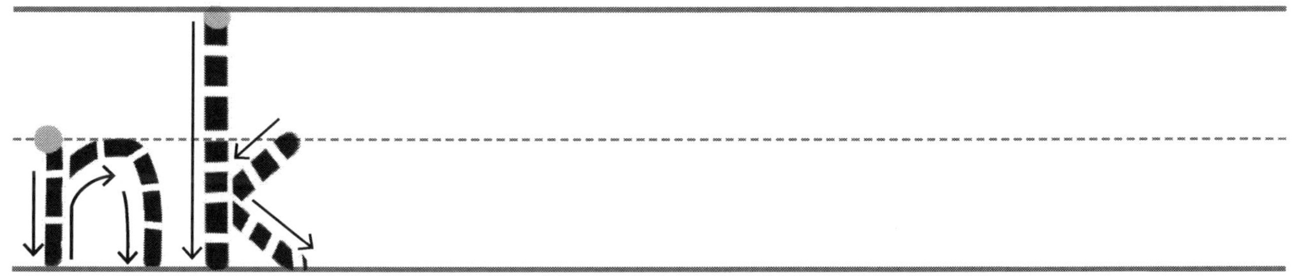

Write the letter ***rack***, ***pack***, ***sack***, and ***raft***.

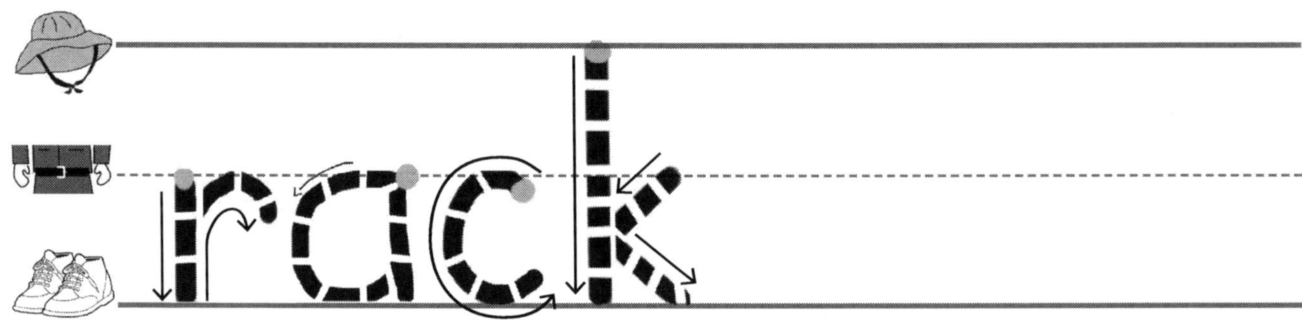

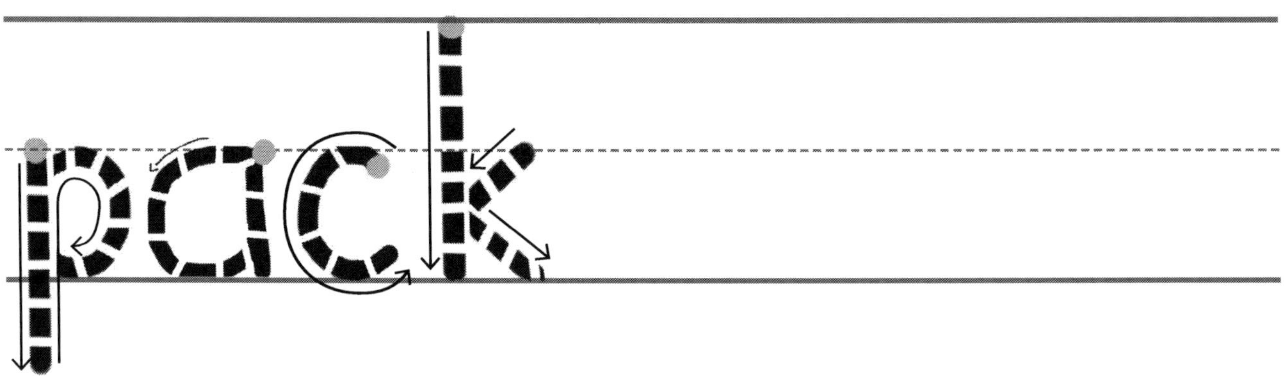

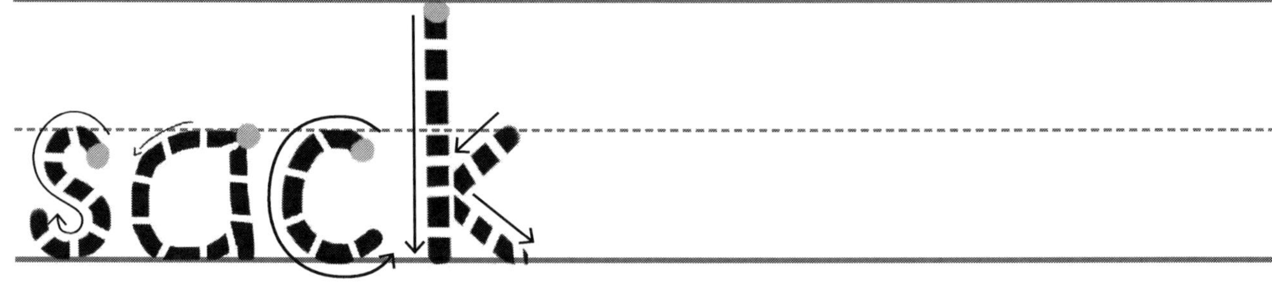

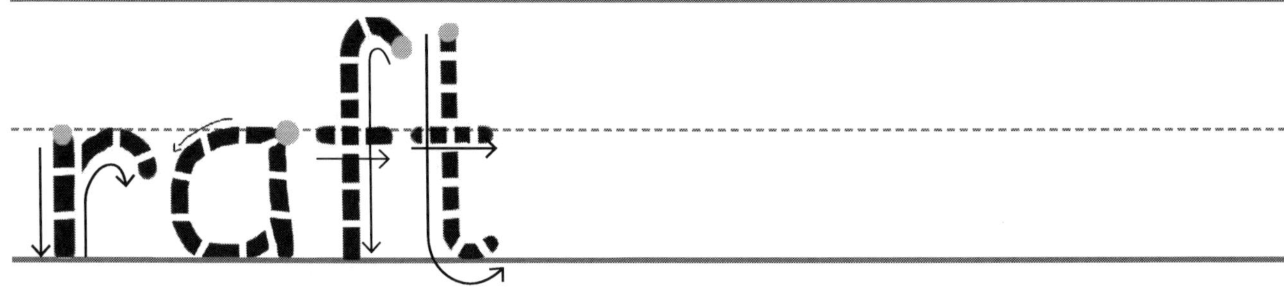

Write a ***K*** under each picture whose name begins like ***kite***.

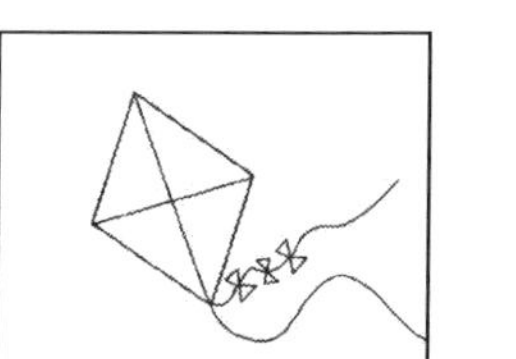

k

1.

2.

3.

4.

5.

6.

7.

8.

9.

Name each picture. If the picture begins with the sound k, draw a line to the kite. If it ends with the sound k, draw a line to the book.

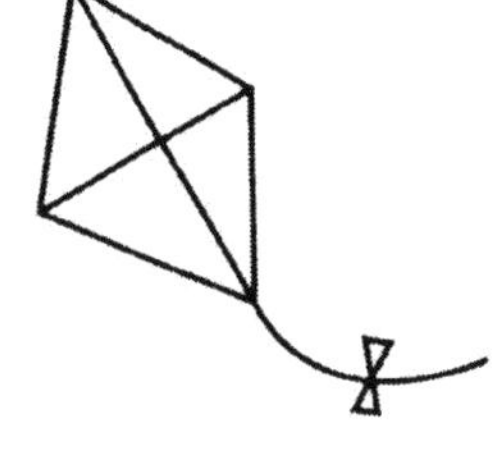

kite

book

Say the name of the picture. Where do you hear the sound of /k/ ***or*** k/ck? Draw a circle around the first ***k*** if t is the beginning sound (as in ***kite***). Draw a circle around ***ck*** if it is the ending sound (as in ***lock***).

Kk | _ck

1.  k ck

2. k ck

3. k ck

4. k ck

5. k ck

6. k ck

Say the name of each picture. Color the picture whos name has the same ending sound as ***lock***. Write the letters ***ck***.

1.

2.

3.

Read the word and the sentence.
Draw a picture about the sentence.

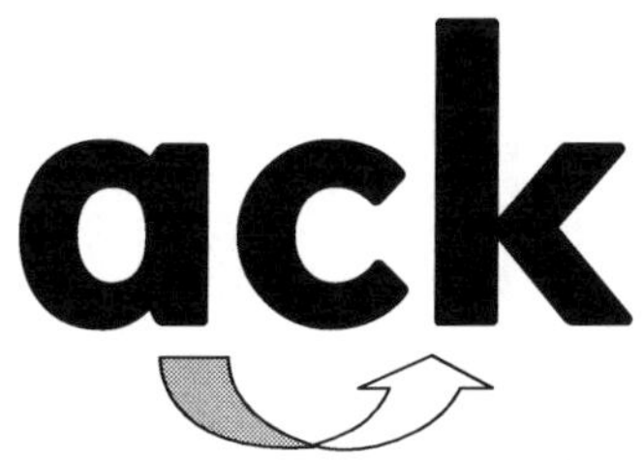

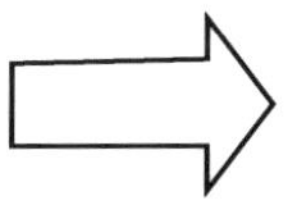

ack

s ack	I have a red <u>sack</u> in my hand.
p ack	I have a yellow <u>pack</u> of rags.

Read the word, tap out the sounds of the word. Then, circle the number of sounds and write the word on the line.

Word	Sounds	Write
pack	1 2 3 4 5	
rack	1 2 3 4 5	
tack	1 2 3 4 5	
sack	1 2 3 4 5	

Cut out the vowel. Paste it onto a stick. Use the stick to practice blending the vowel before and after each consonant.

a

______	g	______
______	t	______
______	h	______
______	f	______
______	p	______
______	s	______
______	c	______
______	ck	

Kk

Cut out the letters on the left. Paste them into the spaces on the right that are **missing letters** to make words.

Make Words

s	n	t
r	p	t
s	d	t
p	s	n
r	m	d
s	d	n
f	f	t

	a	ck
	a	ck
	a	
	a	
	a	
	a	
	a	

Kk

A
B
C

Reading and writing words

has

fad

tag

pack

fan

hand

rack

have

in

yellow

Read the sentences below.
Use your crayon to add details to the pictures.

Sand is on my hand.

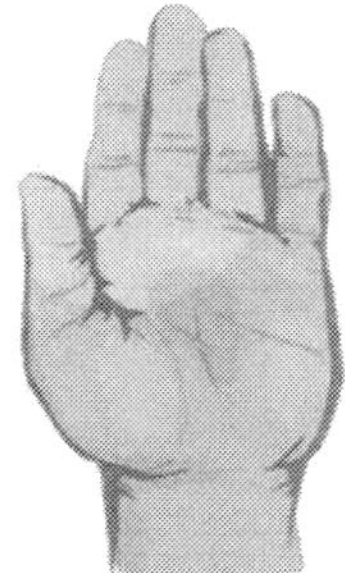

I have sand in my red cap.

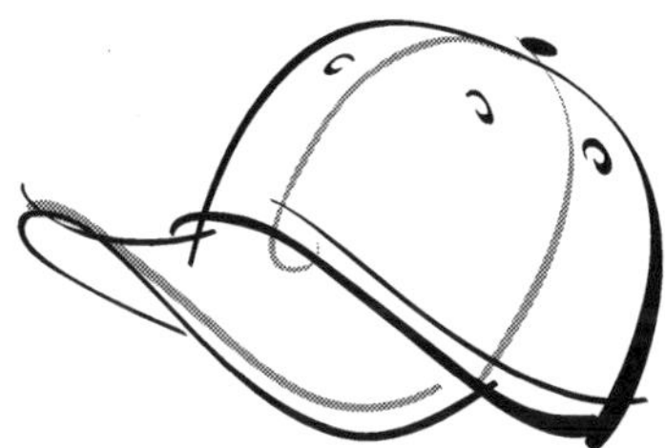

You have sand on the yellow fan.

Sight Words

in	on in no
have	have has his
yellow	yellow you yoo

Circle the sight words;

with fan fat pack hat

red have yellow hand sand

fad no ham cap in

Read the sentences below.
Draw a picture about the sentence.

Fran and Sam have yellow caps.

Fran	Sam

Ann has a red fan. Nan has a yellow fan.

Ann	Nan

Read the sentences below.

1. Gaff ran with the fan.

2. Mack said we can tan.

3. The man has gas for you.

4. Are you on my mat?

5. My hat is on my fat cat.

6. Han can add.

7. We cannot nag at dad.

Read the sentences. Draw a picture of one of the sentences.

1. A man said, “We can pat the cat.”
2. Dad said, “The fat cat sat on the mat.”
3. We sat on the hat!
4. You have the map.
5. I like that pan!

Read the sentences. Draw a line under the word ***have*** in each sentence.

I have a cat.

You have a cat.

You and I have a cat.

Say the word at the beginning of each row. Draw a circle around the word where you see it in the same row.

Name____________________________________

we	we	my
have	and	have
you	you	my
are	are	have

Look at the socks on the clothesline. Sort them into ***pairs*** by drawing a line between matching socks. Color the page.

Look at the mittens on this page. Draw lines to match each pair. Then, color each pair a different color.

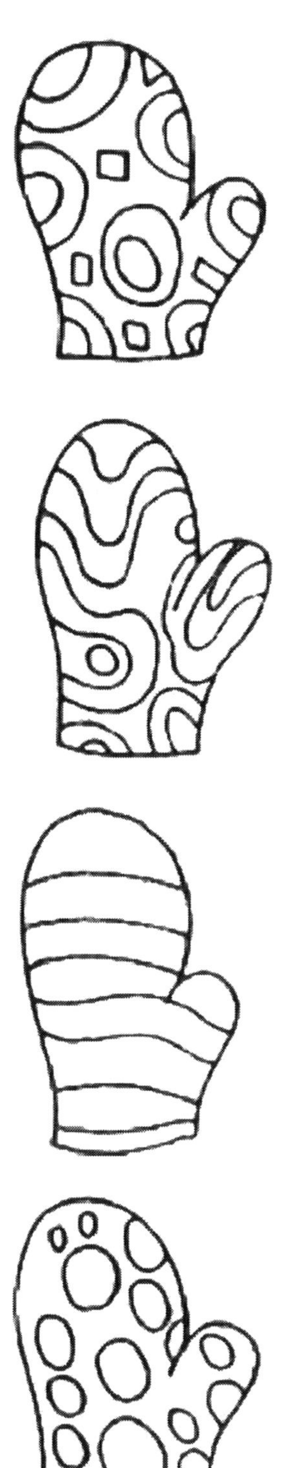

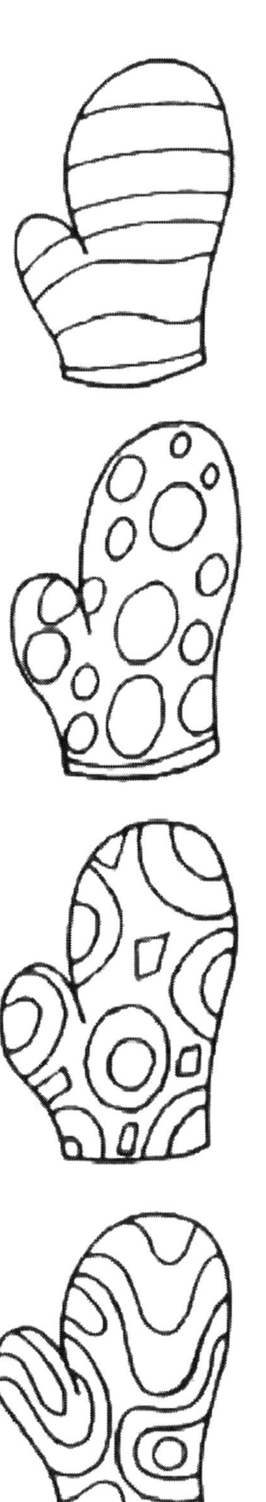

Color the capital ***K's*** green. Color the lower case ***k's*** grey.

K k K k

K k K K K k

K K K K k

K K K k K k

K K k k K k k

Practice the letter ***K***.

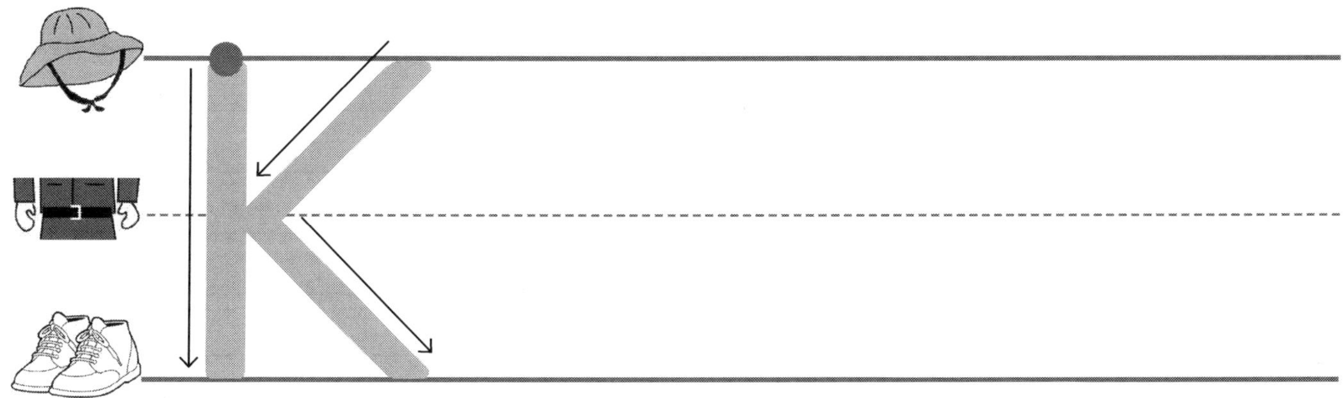

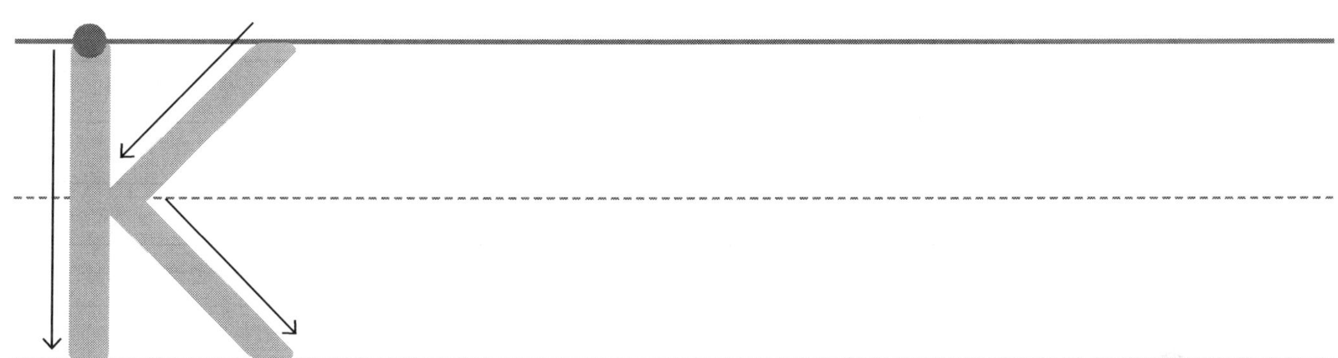

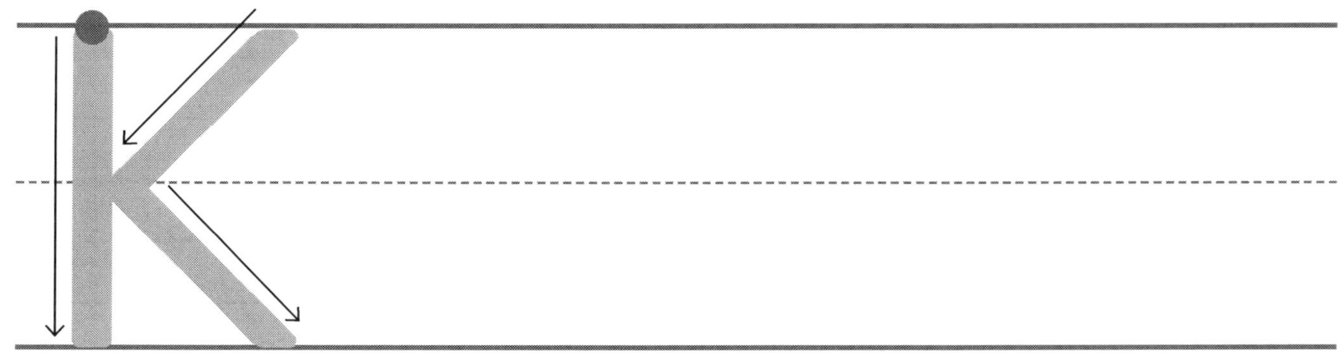

Kk

Practice the letter ***K***.

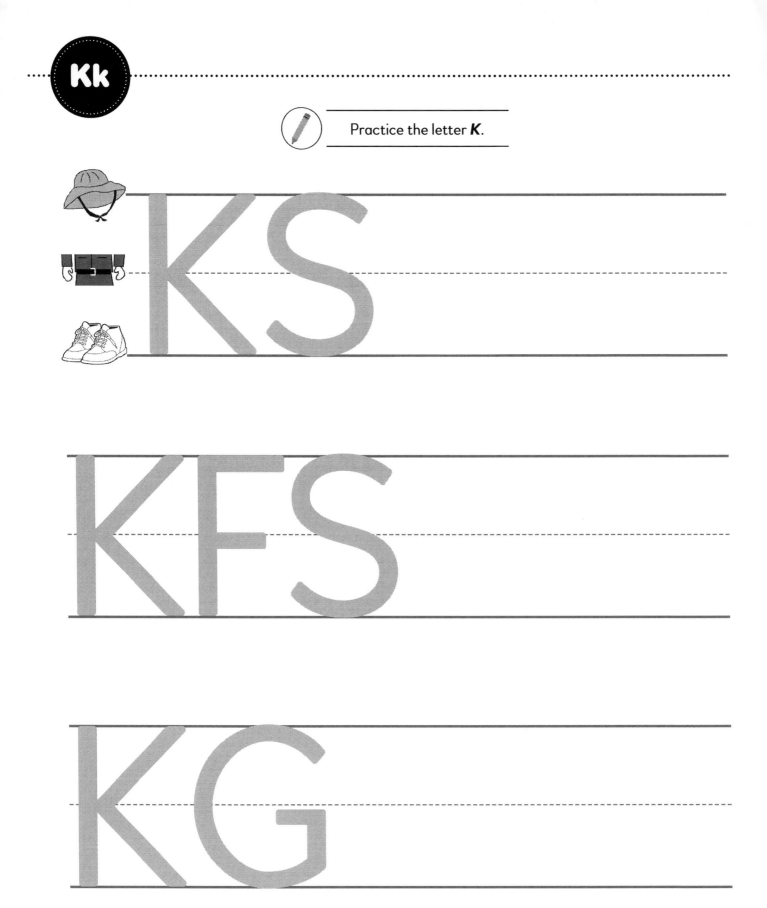

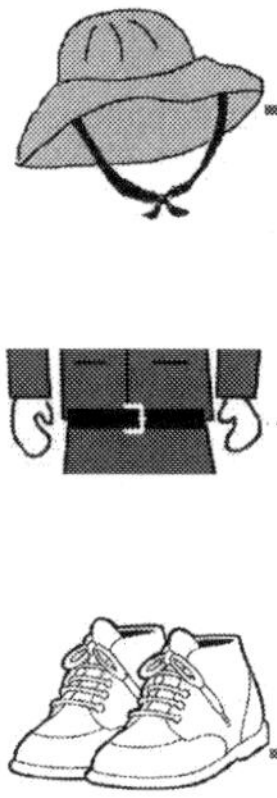

KS

KFS

KG

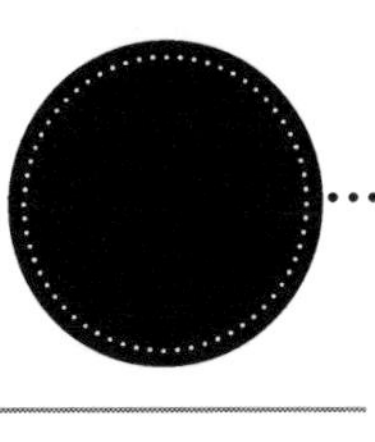

Aa

Nn

Rr

Dd

Mm

Pp

Ss

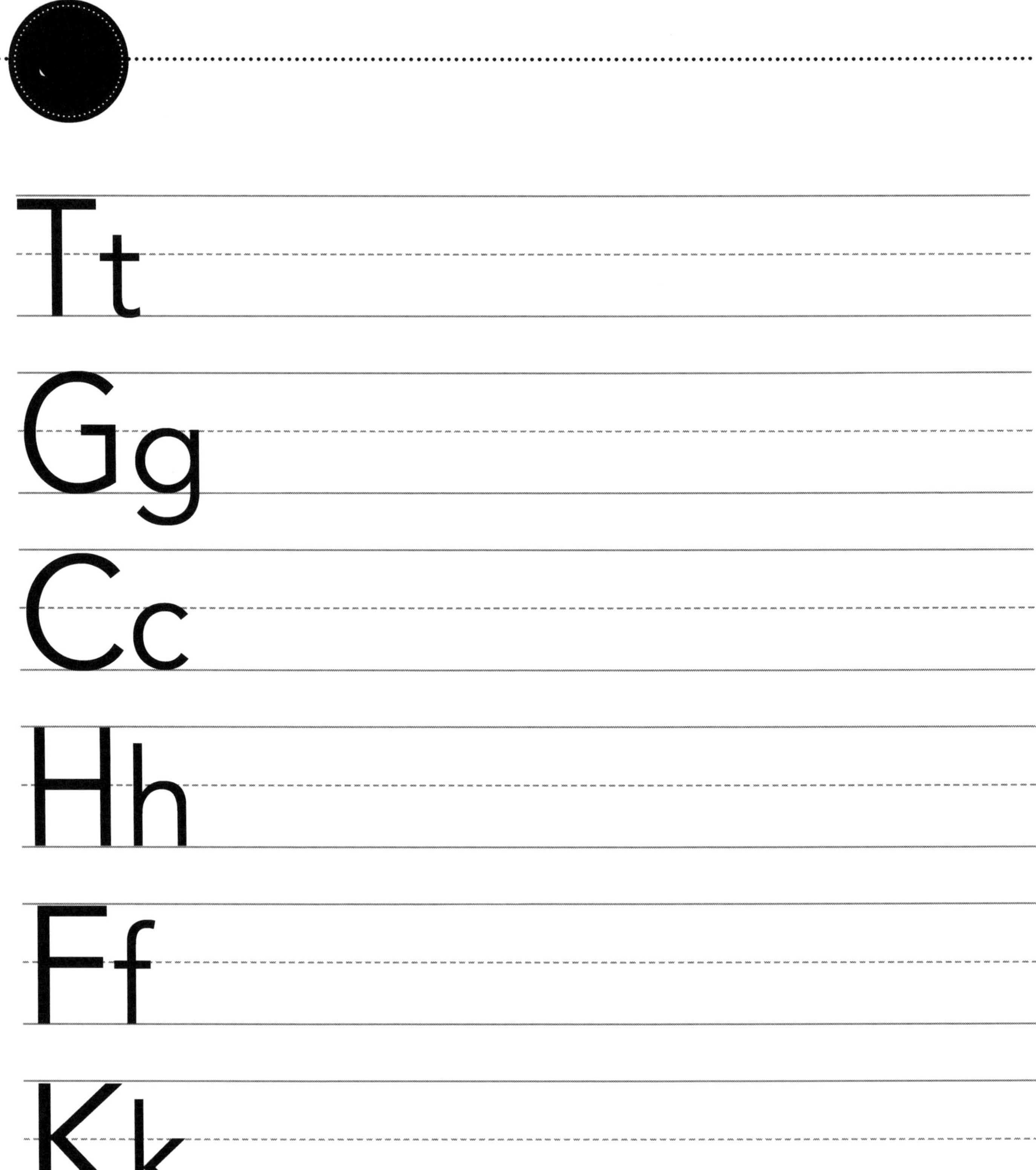
Tt
Gg
Cc
Hh
Ff
Kk

Made in the USA
Lexington, KY
22 November 2019

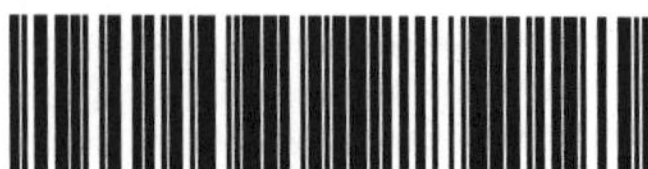

57461996R00109